The Toolbank Collection

Historic Tools

Cover and Title Page:

Plough Plane

C. 1880

A sophisticated design that evolved from the 17th Century out of moulding and rabbet planes, and was used to cut grooves. Made of beechwood, boxwood and lignum vitae.

Legend to the Photographic Plates

Captions preceded by a numeral are supported by a description in the text.
Captions in italics, preceded by an alphabet letter, refer to tools not described in the text.

	b	c
a		d
g	f	e

a. Oveloe Sash Shave with two ⅝ins. irons, Buck
b. Spirit Blow Lamp, Roarer 8B, G. Banthel
c. 7½ins. Norris Steel Wood Smoother
d. Side Fillister, of European origin, with brass adjustable fence and depth stop
e. Socket Brushing Hook, William Swift of Seal, Kent
f. Sharpening Stone in a wooden holder, dated 1793
g. 8ins. Mitre Plane, dovetailed wrought iron with rosewood infill, Buck

A TOOLBANK Publication

First Published 1998 ISBN 1 900269 09 0
Scorpion Cavendish Ltd
31 Museum Street London WC1A 1LH England

Design: Adrian Knowles and Kathi Huidobro
Text: Warwick Knowles Editor: Robert Rowe

Printed and bound in England:
Lawrence-Allen, Weston-super-Mare, Avon

FOREWORD

THE TOOLBANK COLLECTION

John Twallin

As we approach the 21st Century, the Toolbank Museum, from which the tools described in The Toolbank Collection have been selected, enables us to look back one, two and in some cases three centuries and once more to draw satisfaction from tools which were well made, well used and well cared for by several generations. Tools which have withstood the test of time, and which have paid for themselves time and time again.

The world of tools and their uses is far too big a subject for anyone to claim to know it well. The Toolbank Collection is not put forward by experts, but by enthusiasts, well aware that there is always more to learn, and much fun and interest to be had in doing so. It should not be interpreted as a definitive guide to old tools, nor should it be regarded as authoritative.

It is a publication by enthusiasts who cannot look at buildings, furniture or at virtually any conceivable product created by man without wondering as to the type of tools used in their crafting.

Enthusiasm is a by-word for the Toolbank Museum's curator, the compiler and composer of The Toolbank Collection, Wally Flude. It is he whose enthusiasm has made possible the assembling of those tools illustrated in The Toolbank Collection and all of us at Toolbank express our heartfelt thanks to him for his hard work and dedication.

There is many a tool in the Toolbank Museum which Wally has used in his own workshop to prove that it works well. His assistance too at Toolbank in the testing of new products, and advice on modifications which might improve them, continues to be invaluable. Wally's support and interest have been appreciated by many within Toolbank, as well as by me as a personal friend.

We would like to thank Warwick Knowles and Adrian Knowles for writing and putting the book together, Robert Rowe for editing, Pinpoint for photography, and Scorpion Cavendish for publishing: each has given great support to Wally. In thanking them all for their efforts, we hope that The Toolbank Collection, produced by tool people for tool people, will be a book of interest for those with an interest in tools.

July 1998

ABOUT THE TOOLBANK MUSEUM

The foundation of the Toolbank Museum several years ago did not owe itself to any specific strategic decision. There were, however, many reasons why it made sense then, and why it continues to be of enormous relevance to us today.

As tool people, selling quality tools, there could be no better illustration of why it pays to buy a quality product than to look at tools which have lasted for so long, often for hundreds of years, and given such value for money.

It is fascinating to have an insight into the evolution of tools, and to compare those which we sell today with those produced by earlier generations. Perhaps above all it is true today, no less than yesterday, that there is much to be gleaned from the origin and recognition of the value of a 'good name'.

Many of the features which go nowadays into a quality tool – such as steel specification, forging, heat treatment and annealing – cannot be seen by the naked eye, any more than the qualities of the tools of yesteryear could then be perceived. But in these days when many DIY enthusiasts may be attracted by display cartoning, or even by the cheaper end of competitively priced tools, it is a useful reminder that the quality of a product is best understood by specialists in those products who can provide advice and guidance on the integrity and provenance of the products and of their manufacture.

Introduction

THE TOOLBANK COLLECTION

Wally Flude, Curator, Toolbank Museum

"It is very exciting to hold in one's hands an old, often dirty and nearly always much used tool which, upon cleaning, can often reveal a name and possibly even an address. This enables us to trace the years in which the maker traded and in some cases to recall that tools were made and sold, for example, in Lincoln's Inn Fields, Soho, Covent Garden and Westminster, to name but a few. In one's hands is a tool that has given good service to generations of craftsmen over perhaps 200 years, enabling them to practice their craft and earn their living. In many ways, each is a timeless treasure.

The pieces displayed in the Toolbank Museum have been obtained from auctions, sale rooms, dealers, boot fairs, antique and even junk shops, and from many friends and customers who have kindly donated tools.

We have tried in the Toolbank Museum to make our collection as varied and interesting as possible, without becoming too involved in the 'niceties' of the antique trade.

What you see in The Toolbank Collection is a small selection of the tools on display in the Toolbank Museum, to which, I am pleased to report, items are being added at fairly frequent intervals.

Visitors to the Toolbank Museum, by prior appointment only please, are always welcome."

July 1998

Contents

Foreword
John Twallin iii

About The Toolbank Museum iii

Introduction
Wally Flude, Curator, Toolbank Museum iv

Saws 1

Planes 15

Tools for Boring 31

Coopers & Wheelwrights Tools 39

Shipwrights Tools 47

Measuring & Marking 51

Leather Workers Tools 59

Levels 63

Chisels & Axes 67

Spanners & Wrenches 71

An Amalgam of Tools & Small Machines 75

Hammers, Screwdrivers & Turnscrews 85

The Toolbank Museum 88

Bibliography 91

Index 92

Saws

THE TOOLBANK COLLECTION

Saw handle; carving detail

Spear & Jackson saw; branded for Humphris & Son

Marples panel saw; brass facing and rivets

Cross cut saw; engraver's art

Saw-like tools have had a very long ancestry stretching back 9,000 years into the Neolithic era, though they developed more slowly than the ubiquitous axe. None of the early sawing implements could cut right through a piece as a modern saw does, so the consensus of opinion is that such pre-Metal Age cutting tools can be regarded as serrated knives or scrapers for severing or fraying off material.

The true saw began to take on the familiar modern toothed shape when the ancient world had accumulated sufficient experience in casting bronze and iron. The Egyptians, who worked with bronze from about 1500BC and then the Assyrians several hundred years later, using iron, were able to cast blades that were thin enough to cut wood and hard enough to saw stone. These early saws must have required considerable patience to use. They had neither the ductility of worked iron or steel nor would they withstand being pushed without buckling. Saws of this early period were all designed as pull saws, having sharply raked teeth which faced towards the heel. The attainable limit for any length of blade was about 12-14ins. A gentle curve to the toothed edge was found to ease resistance in the kerf, but additional wedging open was usually required to minimise friction.

Nevertheless, the saw was one of the great innovations of the Metal Age. The Romans overcame the two problems of clearing waste and lowering friction by setting the teeth to create a saw slot wider than the thickness of the blade. They were able to make much longer blades too. By tensioning a long blade within a wooden frame it became possible to work the saw in both directions even though it was not strictly a push saw. The first backed handsaws were also of Roman origin.

Saw design since then made relatively slow progress until the Industrial Revolution when rolling mills were devised that could produce steel in sheet form. The saws in The Toolbank Collection are post Industrial Revolution and date from the 19th Century onwards. They show a great diversity of design and refinement to suit the tasks to which they were put (such as cutting salt!) and remain a testament to the skills of their makers.

French Armchair Makers Saw

Mid 19th Century

This tool has an unexpected shape for a saw. For a start it has handles on it that are more typical of a plane. The saw blade is approximately an inch deep and is embedded into the side of a wooden stock that is about 10ins. long. At first glance one might think it is some sort of edging tool or designed to cut fine grooves.

The tool's shape has, however, derived from its specific use and working technique in cutting tenons on curved members of armchairs. The Armchair Makers Saw, used in conjunction with a top box cramp, provided nineteenth century furniture makers with a simple technique for cutting tenon shoulders to any angle on a chair arm and ensured a perfect fit with the mortice in the chair back.

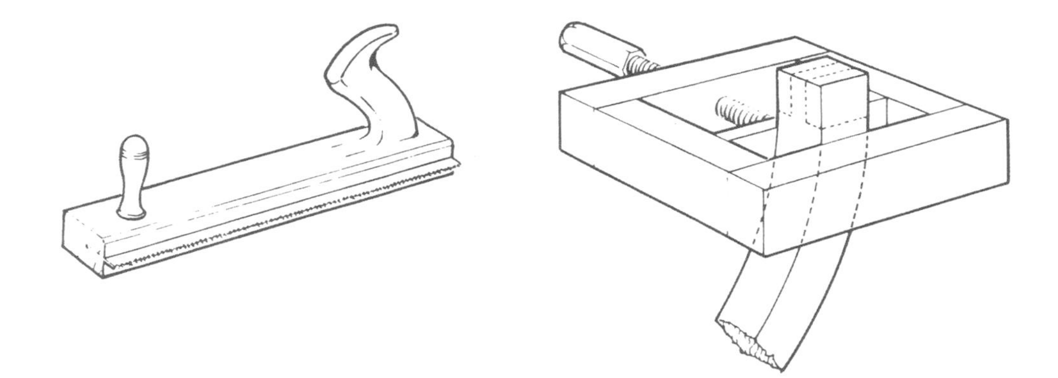

The top box cramp, typically about six inches square and made of 2 x 2ins. wood with a screw cramp in one side, was probably fitted into a workbench for example, to extend the flat working surface. The arm piece was held in the cramp with sufficient length exposed above the table surface for the cheeks and shoulders to be marked out with a template. The shoulders were then cut by drawing the saw sideways, across the work surface.

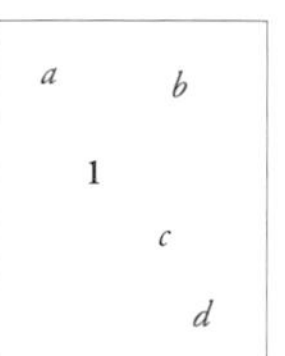

1. French Armchair Makers Saw

a. Wooden Compasses
b. Double Iron Shave, C.Nurse
c. Small Hacksaw
d. 12ins. 4-Fold Ivory Rule, J. Rabone & Sons

Saws

THE TOOLBANK COLLECTION

The trio of saws shows 19th Century refinement of the straight cutting edge "English Pattern", which had become firmly established in this country a century and a half earlier. Each saw is taper ground. Good quality saws were traditionally ground 'four gauges thin to back' to give sufficient clearance.

Disston Handsaw with Finger Hole

Henry Disston & Sons

Late 19th Century

A characteristic skew back rip saw of 28ins. made by Henry Disston, with incremental teeth (teeth graduated in size and frequency from head to toe and sharpened with a chisel point). The first few teeth at the toe are often sharpened to cross-cut shape for better cutting when a knot is encountered. His skew back design, introduced in 1874, uses apple as the preferred wood for the handles. This handle is firmly fixed with five rivets and has a finger hole to provide a stronger grip.

Henry Disston, who remains one of the most famous saw makers, learned his trade with Spear & Jackson before emigrating to America where he began manufacturing his own saws in Philadelphia in 1840. At that time most tools were imported into America from England. Henry Disston reversed the trend exporting from premises in Toronto, Canada.

Marples Panel Saw

William Marples & Sons

Late 19th Century

A 26ins. panel saw with the teeth sharpened to cross-cut form. It has two 'visual aids' for the carpenter. One side of the back has an engraved rule marked out in inches with sixteenths sub-divisions. The front end of the handle is brass faced and firmly riveted with four rivets to make a right angle with the back. The 'angle guide' has become a popular feature nowadays on many makes of saw.

Buck Half Rip Saw

Buck

Late 19th Century

A 27ins. half rip saw with incremental teeth. The nib on the back is traditional and there has been much speculation as to its purpose. The Curator believes it is simply a stop for a tie string, so that a tooth guard can be secured from slipping off at the point. The other end of the guard would be tied round the handle bow.

It is not certain where, or when, the term 'half rip' originated. The term probably arose in the last century as a colloquial expression to indicate length as well as function. A rip saw for cutting along the grain (i.e. a saw with chisel cut teeth) was 28-30ins. long. Rip saws between 26-28ins. were known as 'half rips'. Handsaws shorter than 26ins. were called 'panel saws' and have angle cut teeth for cutting across the grain.

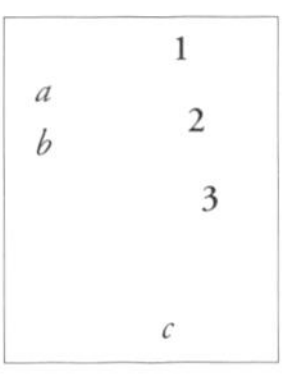

1. Disston Handsaw
2. Marples Panel Saw
3. Buck Half Rip Saw

a. 10ins. Compass Saw
b. 5ins. Compass Saw
c. 24ins. Handsaw showing ornately carved handle

Wooden Frame Saw

Mid 19th Century

A wooden framed saw for cross cutting and curved work which uses the saw blade on the outside edge. The 27ins. frame follows the typical pattern favoured in England where the stretcher across the middle is sub-tenonned in a loose fit with the side arms. On the continent the stretcher is more often attached to the arms with a dowel link. A significant difference in this example is the use of a tensioning wire and turn buckle instead of the traditional leather thong and tensioning stick.

Pine & Steel Bettye Saw

Early 19th Century

A pine framed 'Bettye' or Betty Saw – so called because when used in the vertical position it "danced like Betty". Found in chairmakers' or wheelwrights' shops and generally user made, it was used for cutting 'felloes' (or 'fellys', the curved pieces of wood which joined together to form a rim) and also for ripping boards. There are several ways of tensioning the blade. This example uses a threaded link and wing nut.

The patterns of both these saws have remained virtually unchanged since biblical times and are still preferred in some countries. Carpenters can hand make their own frames and need only buy the blade. The style of the Wooden Frame Saw is known in Italy as a 'St. Joseph's Saw'. Longer versions of the Betty Saw will rip down balks of timber.

Artillery Chain Saw

Early 20th Century

This rather sinister looking artillery saw is 44ins. overall and made up of 53 segments a little over ¾ins. long. The very piercing teeth vary in height and are not uniformly set but are ideal for dealing quickly with green wood in a field situation. It is easily pitched over a branch with a rope fixed at either end and can be worked back and forth by one person, or by one or two pulling on each rope. It would make a very effective pruning saw.

Don Smith, a friend of the Curator, who donated the saw, remembers using a similar one with a 'D' shaped handle at each end when he was a paratrooper. It was standard equipment and was carried on the belt in a green webbing pouch.

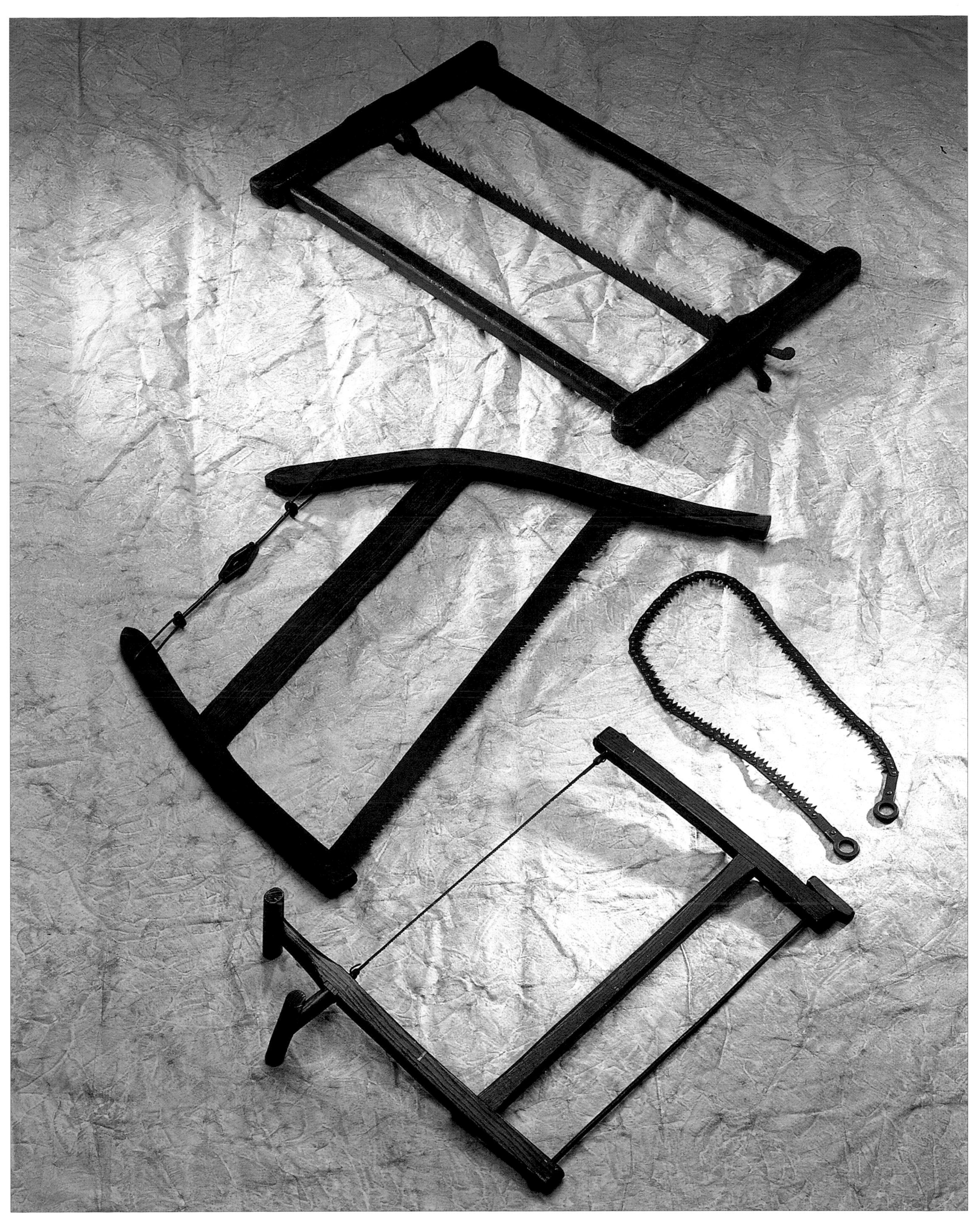

1	
2	3
a	

1. Pine & Steel Bettye Saw
2. Wooden Frame Saw
3. Artillery Chain Saw

a. Coach Builders Saw

5IN PIANO MAKERS SAW
Buck & Co.
C.1850

This smallest saw in the collection is also known as a Toy Saw (the use of the word here meaning 'small'). It is capable of very intricate work in confined spaces. The Piano Makers Saw retains the look of a push saw rather than a saw-knife for it pre-dates the modern style of padsaw or keyhole saw. The open handle has just about enough room to take the four fingers of one's hand though it is more comfortable and manoeuvrable if gripped with three fingers only, leaving the little finger to nestle under the crook'd horn. Extra downward pressure can be created by placing the thumb along the top edge of the handle.

16IN SALT SAW
W.H. Fagan & Son
Late 19th Century

The presence of a Salt Saw in the collection is an intriguing novelty in an age where salt comes 'free flowing' out of a container. Such saws must have been commonplace in every ironmongers when salt was sold in blocks. The blade, which is quite thick, has coarse teeth and is made of zinc in order to resist corrosion. There is enough rigidity in the blade for sawing but it is so malleable that it can be bent almost at right angles and still be straightened out again. Stronger and more expensive models were made with copper blades, though they would have required regular polishing to thwart discolouration.

The Curator has been unable to find any reference to the makers, W.H. Fagan & Son, so we have no idea where they were based or if they made any other type of tool.

16IN BRASS BACKED TENON SAW
Henry Disston & Sons
Early 20th Century

The Disston Brass Backed Tenon Saw has a very aesthetically pleasing look. A very fine fleam toothed design which brings to mind the following words found on every Disston saw:

"For Beauty, Finish and Utility
this Saw cannot be Excelled."

The phrase has become the motto for 150 years of Disston quality tools.

SLIDING DOVETAIL GROOVING SAW
19th Century

Specialist saws like this one (sometimes called 'stair builders' saws') originated on the continent in the 18th Century. They are characteristically individual in shape with decorated side cheeks. Some are designed as push saws, others as pull saws, but they are not well known in this country. This example is French.

Its function is to cut the sides of a groove across the grain for dovetailing. The wooden stock on this example is angled upwards from the blade, on each side, to obtain the correct wall angle for the female part of the dovetail.

VINE PRUNING SAW
C.1900

A vine pruning saw of French origin which has evidently been locally crafted with pride, the blade having been fitted into an antler handle. An interesting feature is the open hook at the blade point, which would help to extend the pruner's reach so that selected growths can be gathered for cutting. The hook may partly serve to prevent the blade slipping out of a cut. Some modern pruning knives have a similar adaptation where the hook is turned in towards the toothed edge.

1		
	2	
4		
		3
5		
	a	

1. 16ins. Brass Backed Tenon Saw
2. 16ins. Salt Saw
3. Vine Pruning Saw
4. 5ins. Piano Makers Saw
5. Sliding Dovetail Grooving Saw

a. Masons Jointing Tool, William Marples

4IN JEWELLERS PIERCING SAW

C.1800

A very elegant design with a beautifully turned ebony handle and brass ferrule. The blade locks in a fixed position but the bow provides enough clearance for alteration of the blade direction when working on small pieces. In precision tools like this, it is important to maintain the correct setting of blade tension. Tension is manually adjusted by the wing nut and collar holding the bow. The small horn at the front acts as a thumb rest to aid precision in use.

SAW SETS

Most handsaws are 'sprung set' to provide clearance for the saw blade and prevent binding of the saw in cuts. Spring setting is to bend the teeth slightly outwards at an angle, alternate teeth left and right. Before setting the teeth in this manner two other operations, 'jointing' and 'shaping' should have been carried out. Jointing cuts the points of the highest teeth down to the level of the lowest points so that all the teeth are the same height and will cut equally. Shaping files the face and top of each tooth sharp, to make the appropriate cutting point for a rip or cross-cut saw.

Setting may be done in many ways from freehand and by eye, using a punch and hammer, to the many machines shown below. Each one has a different method of creating the uniform bend in the teeth.

ECLIPSE SAW SET

C.1900

The No.77 Pattern by Eclipse is a plier type saw set in gunmetal.

ANVIL SAW SET

C.1850

In the anvil type the striker is hit by a hammer, the tooth being bent to an equal angle between the striker and the anvil.

MORRELLS PATTERN SAW SET

C.1853

The Morrell's Pattern plier type was made by E. Preston & Sons circa 1853.

GATE TYPE SAW SET

C.1900

This gate type saw set dates from the turn of the century and has a sliding brass fence. The appropriate slot and gate is fitted over the tooth and levered to the correct angle indicated by the fence.

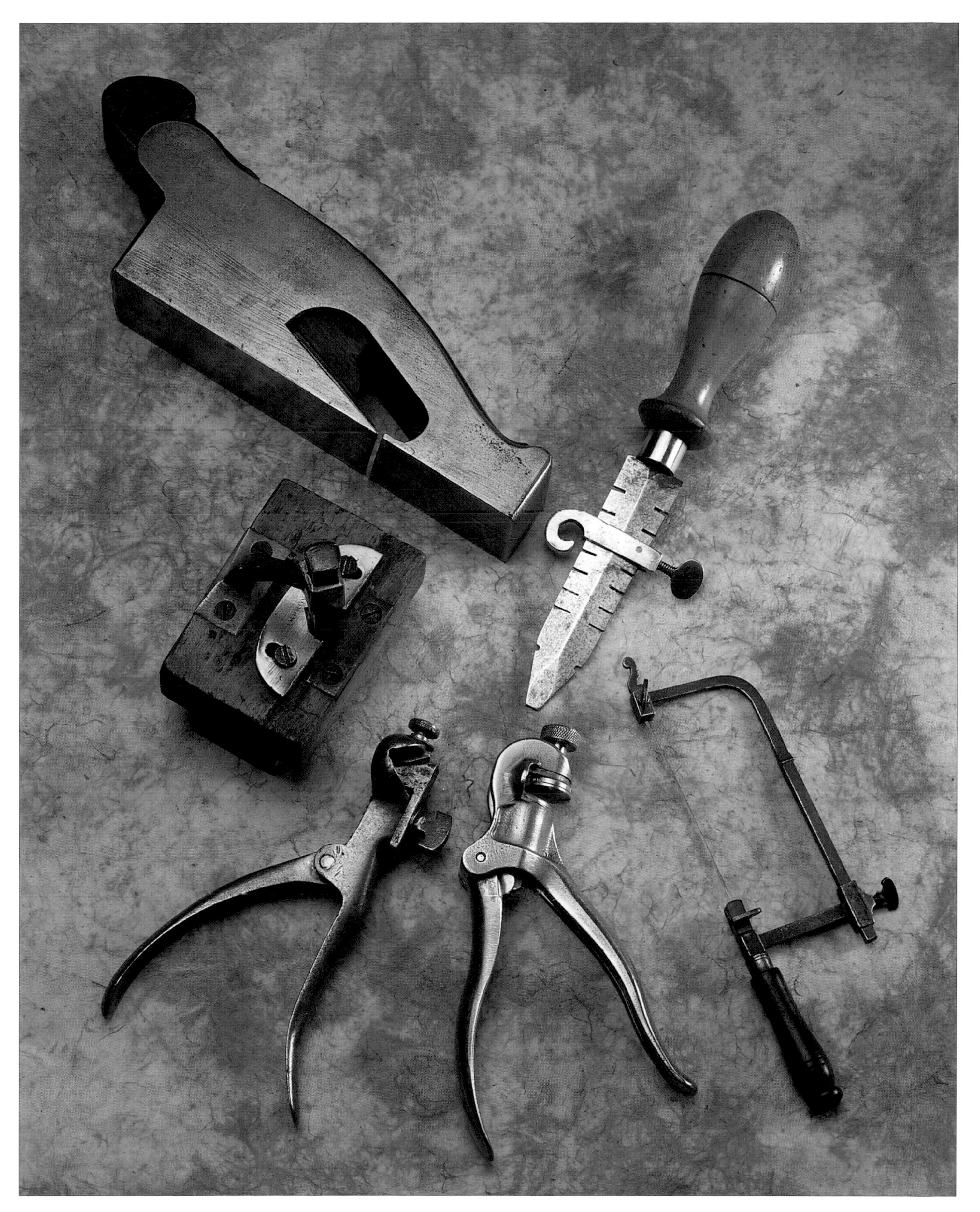

a		
1	2	
5	4	3

1. Anvil Saw Set
2. Gate Type Saw Set
3. 4ins. Jewellers Piercing Saw
4. Eclipse Saw Set
5. Morrells Pattern Saw Set

a. Skew Shoulder Plane

Atkins Saw Set

C.1880

The Atkins Saw Set is an anvil type held in a vice. The saw blade is moved along between the striker and anvil so that the teeth are positioned under the striker. Hitting the striker with a hammer sets the teeth to a fixed angle.

Brass Hacksaw

Early 20th Century

An hacksaw which is probably of U.S. origin.

5in Hacksaw

Late 19th Century

A small 5ins. hacksaw for detail work made by J. Heyes.

Pruning Saw/Chopper

Late 19th Century

This is a much more robust pruning tool than the one shown on page 8. The heavy 20ins. blade is sharpened on one edge for chopping and on the opposite edge for sawing.

Lancashire Pattern Hacksaw

Buck & Hickman

Early 20th Century

A "Lancashire Pattern" frame hacksaw by Buck & Hickman.

22in Panel Saw

Spear & Jackson

C.1910-1915

An example of retailer branding. The Humphris & Son identity has been engraved alongside Spear & Jackson's own motif. The saw is a 22ins. skew back and taper with 8 points to the inch. The eventual owner evidently took the precaution of adding a brass reinforcing plate underneath the handle.

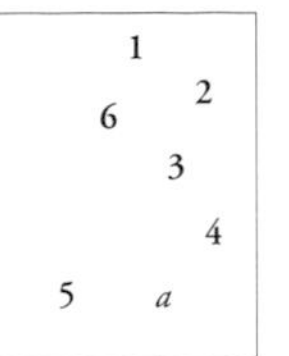

1. Lancashire Pattern Hacksaw, Buck & Hickman
2. 22ins. Panel Saw, Spear & Jackson
3. Pruning Saw/Chopper
4. 5ins. Hacksaw, J. Heyes
5. Atkins Saw Set
6. Brass Hacksaw

a. Sheep Shears

Saws

Saw Sharpening Vice

C.1900

A brass saw sharpening vice mounted on a hardwood back, which has a decorative finish typical of the Art Nouveau period. It is approximately 12ins. in length and the brass jaws have the capacity to accommodate the full depth of the saw. The saw is cramped with a lever action. The hardwood 'tongue' is gripped in an upright position in the bench vice.

Swivel Vice with Anvil

Late 19th Century

This steel vice is designed to swivel from side to side and was probably used by a model maker or instrument maker. It has $2\frac{1}{2}$ins. jaws and an anvil behind the fixed jaw.

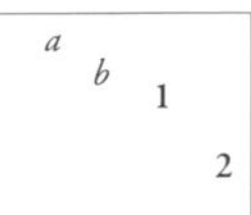

1. Saw Sharpening Vice
2. Swivel Vice with Anvil

a. $\frac{3}{16}$ins. Coachmakers Jigger/Router
b. Double Coach Router

PLANES

THE TOOLBANK COLLECTION

Bailey frog; transition from wooden plane to metal

Dovetailed jointing; brass & steel

Moulding plane; showing box-wood slip

Gunmetal shave; detail

In most modern tools it is possible to make out their origin and descent, but it is peculiarly difficult to do so for the plane. Planes, shaves and scrapers are closely related (the stone scraper being one of the earliest of human tools). Of these, the plane achieves precise cutting control and makes surfaces true.

The plane could have been a genuine innovation, though a form of wedged adze, or perhaps of drawing knife, may have been precursors. The adze was the best method of giving wood a sufficiently smooth surface, other than the ancient Egyptians' skillful use of stone abrasives. Neither approach could obtain the perfection of a planed surface.

By whatever origins, the Romans were already in possession of very sophisticated smoothing and jack planes by the 1st Century AD. They were strikingly similar in size to today's planes. They possessed not only aesthetic appeal, but also considerable craftsmanship, using wood as a stock inlaid with bronze or iron, fixed to an iron sole. It is surprising that such a useful tool did not remain established after the decline of the Roman empire. There is practically no evidence for its existence, or use, for 800 years until the 16th Century. Yet within the following 100 years the plane re-emerged as an essential craftsman's tool and by the 18th Century, plane-making had become an industry in its own right.

The modern cast iron plane has remained virtually unchanged for the whole of this century and that attests to its fitness for purpose. Before that, three significant imperfections were overcome. The first was to alter the way the cutter was wedged, which improved the extraction of shavings. The second was the introduction of a top iron, which regulated shaving thickness so that it curled easily out of the mouth. The third was the elimination of the fixed wedge altogether, so that blade depth could be finely adjusted and lateral movement introduced with a lever cam.

It is remarkable how the plane, as a concept, has translated into such an astonishing variety of types and styles through individual craftsmanship and this is well illustrated here.

SPILL MAKING PLANES

In the days before electricity or even flint lighters, spill planes were an essential household tool to make wooden tapers (spills) for lighting candles, lanterns or one's pipe!

Spill planes are used 'iron up'. A short length of timber or piece of batten is pushed over the plane and a spiralled shaving emerges from the side. The knack is to obtain a steady, well curled shaving which gives the spill strength and a good length – necessary when lighting up from an open hearth!

BEECHWOOD SPILL MAKING PLANE

Early 19th Century

A free-standing beechwood plane with dovetailed legs which produces tightly curled thin spills.

PLAIN SPILL PLANE

Early 19th Century

A hand held version which produces broad, open spills.

PRESTON 'JUNIOR' PATENT SPIRAL SPILL MACHINE

Early 19th Century

A grandiose title for this 'pocket size' model, which is made of cast iron and produces even and finely curled spills.

CLOSED HANDLE MOULDING PLANE

C.1850

This moulding plane has a particularly wide moulding of about 2½ins. using a French iron made by Peugeot Frères. The greater the width the more power is required for cutting and this is reflected in the size of its very sturdy stock. One side of the stock has a stepped wall. It could act as a fence. The handle is provided for better control and a more comfortable grip.

2IN GUNMETAL SHAVE

Late 19th Century

One of the favourite tools in the collection both for its looks and the quality of the casting. This type of tool became popular in America in the last century. The English name 'spokeshave' implies it was primarily a wheelwrights' tool. Shaves are known to have been used in earlier times for smoothing surfaces which had been worked on firstly by adze or axe. The tool may have been developed from the drawing knife.

PLOUGH PLANE WITH IVORY SCALE

C.1830

The plough plane is designed for making grooves and therefore has a narrow iron and stock. On this example the adjusting arms for the fence have nicely finished brass ends. Each arm has an inserted rule of ivory.

SHOULDER OR REBATE PLANE

1894-1900

An 8ins. gunmetal plane with a 1½ins. iron made by E. Preston & Sons at the Whittall Works in Birmingham between 1894 and 1900. It has an ebony infill and wedge.

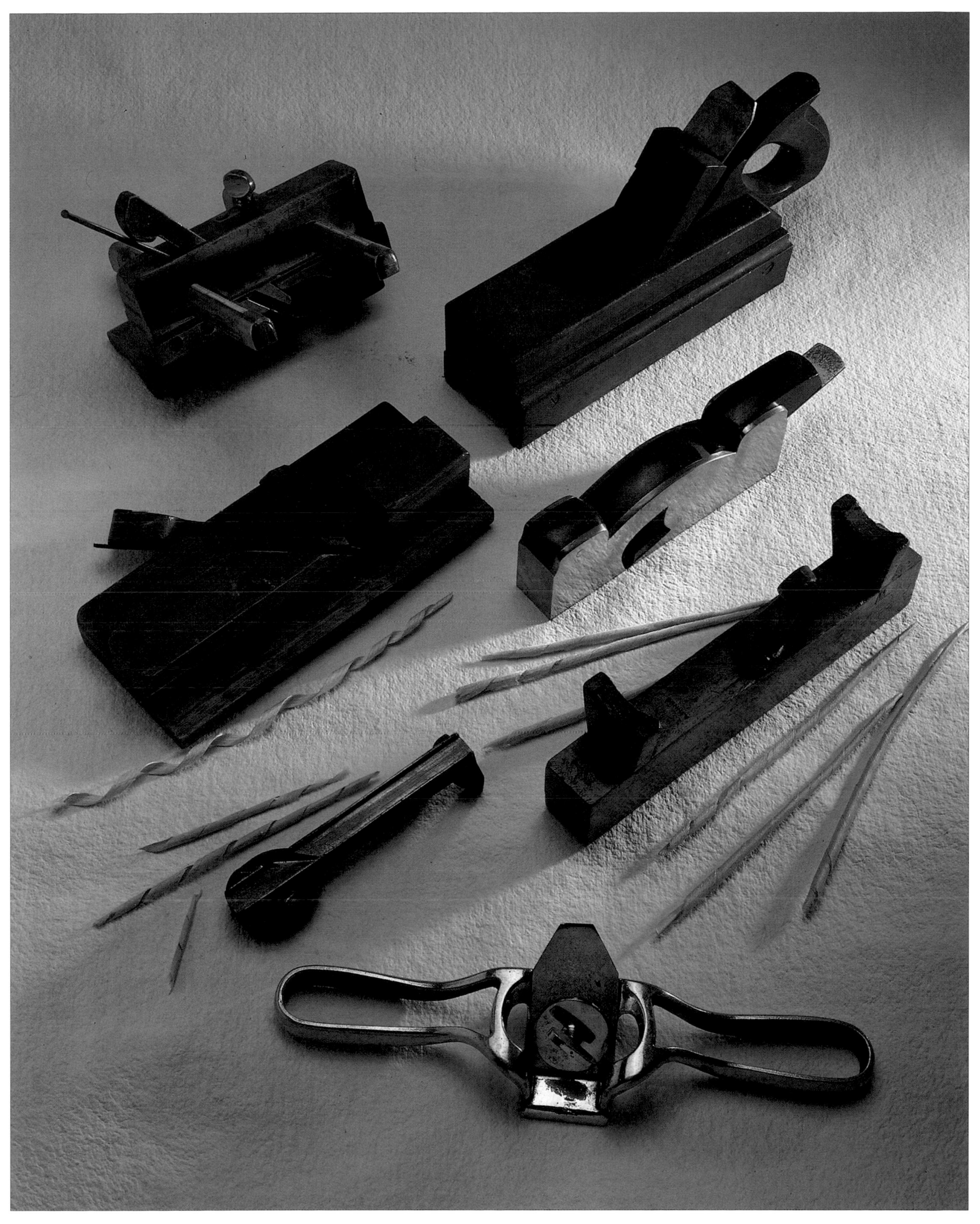

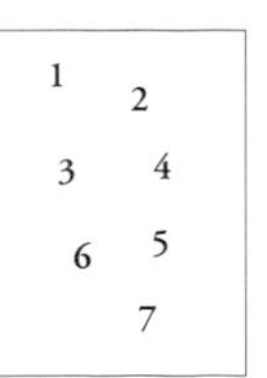

1. Plough Plane with Ivory Scale
2. Closed Handle Moulding Plane
3. Plain Spill Plane
4. Shoulder or Rebate Plane
5. Beechwood Spill Making Plane
6. Preston 'Junior' Patent Spiral Spill Machine
7. 2ins. Gunmetal Shave

ADJUSTABLE COMPASS PLANES

The technical difficulties of creating smooth curved surfaces have exercised many inventive minds. Several solutions to the problem are shown elsewhere in this book, for instance a cooper's sun plane on page 40 and a shipwright's scull plane and mast planes on pages 49-50. Whereas those examples have soles or sides of fixed curvature, the types shown here have been able to utilise a flexible metal sole which introduces the possibility of convex and concave curvature from the same tool. A proven design which continues in use today.

NO.113 ADJUSTABLE COMPASS PLANE
Stanley Rule & Level Co.

C.1879

The Stanley Rule & Level Co. pattern No.113 of 17 June 1879 uses a flexible sole, 1¾ins. wide x 10ins. long, which can be adjusted to create different curves, concave or convex. The toothed cams ensure the same degree of curvature is transmitted 'fore and aft' of the iron using only one adjusting nut at the front. Shown opposite, caption 5.

ADJUSTABLE COMPASS PLANE
I. & H. Sorby

Early 20th Century

A compass plane with a wooden body and flexible sole from Sorby circa 1900-1920. The curvature of the sole has to be adjusted separately at both ends.

HOLLOWS AND ROUNDS
Buck

C.1870

These two half-sets of hollows and rounds are moulding planes made by Buck, Tottenham Court Road, London 1867-1879. They are basic planes for making simple mouldings. There is little difference in the pattern of these planes from those used in the 18th Century.

NO.113 ADJUSTABLE COMPASS PLANE
Stanley Rule & Level Co.

C.1900

A pattern No.113 with later modifications. The model adopts the more contemporary form of lever cap over the cutting iron. Shown opposite, caption 3.

LANCASHIRE PATTERN REBATE PLANE

Late 19th Century

A beautiful example of the vertical iron "Lancashire Pattern" showing its economy of design. The tool must be worked from right to left. Note the very individual shape of the handle.

15½IN DOVETAILED PANEL PLANE
Buck

C.1890

The Buck Dovetailed Panel Plane has a very high order of craftsmanship. The choice of rosewood for the infill and the way the sides have also been shaped and bevelled makes this tool a work of art. 'Dovetailed' refers to the way the steel sole was jointed to the side plates with almost invisible dovetail joints. The 2½ins. iron was supplied by William Marples, the cap iron by Ward. The plane and screw cap were made by Buck, Tottenham Court Road, London, during the ownership of Mrs G. Buck who ran the business from 1880-1930.

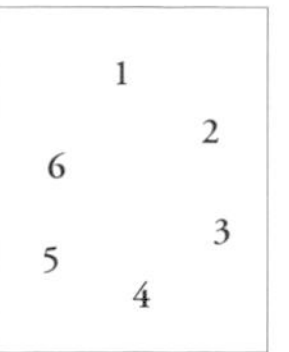

1. Two Half-sets of Hollows & Rounds, Buck
2. Adjustable Compass Plane, I. & H. Sorby
3. Adjustable Compass Plane, Stanley Rule & Level Co.
4. Lancashire Pattern Rebate Plane
5. Adjustable Compass Plane, Stanley Rule & Level Co.
6. 15½ins. Dovetailed Panel Plane, Buck

PLANES

22IN BUCK PANEL PLANE

Buck

C.1890

Constructed of steel with a rosewood infill like the Buck Dovetailed Panel Plane on page 18. Made to special order only.

9½IN T&G COMBINATION PLANE

Mid 19th Century

The combination of two tools into one for tonguing and grooving dates from the 18th Century. This double-ended match plane shows the two irons facing each other in opposite directions. A "push me, pull me" tool for tonguing one way and grooving the other.

NO.8 SWINGING FENCE MATCHING PLANE

Stanley Rule & Level Co.

C.1910

An all metal plane for tonguing and grooving. The fence is pivoted. When swung about, it covers one of the cutters and so produces first a tongue and then, swung the other way, cuts a groove to match.

OPEN MOUTH ROUTERS

C.1880

A pair of beechwood open mouth routers, one with a ⅜ins. iron and the other a ⅝ins. The open mouth provides the user with an unobstructed view.

MOULDING PLANES

The major centre for the plane-making industry in the 18th & 19th Centuries was inner London. It arose from a fascination with Italian decorative moulding – which enchanted those who had the opportunity to do 'The Grand Tour' of Renaissance Italy. The industry peaked around 1850 with the invention of powered mechanical moulding machines and then declined. Various moulding planes are shown and all have interesting names and addresses.Dates given refer to manufacturing periods.

NO.8 BEECHWOOD HOLLOW

William Madox

1748-1775

Peter Street, Westminster, London.

⅜IN BEECHWOOD SIDE BEAD

Moseley & Son

1819-1830

New Street, Covent Garden, London.

NO.4 BEECHWOOD SIDE BEAD

E. Cox

1843-1852

15 Great Queen Street,
Lincoln's Inn Fields, London.

NO.5 BEECHWOOD SQUARE OVAL

I. Sym

1753-1786

Westminster, London.

NO.7 ½IN BEECHWOOD SIDE BEAD

William Shepley

1780-1793

40 Greek Street, Soho, London.

NO.3 BEECHWOOD HOLLOW

William Moss

1775-1848

28 Dudley Street, Birmingham.

⅜IN BEECHWOOD SIDE BEAD

Robert Fitkin

1750-1778

Bridgewater Gardens, Barbican, London.

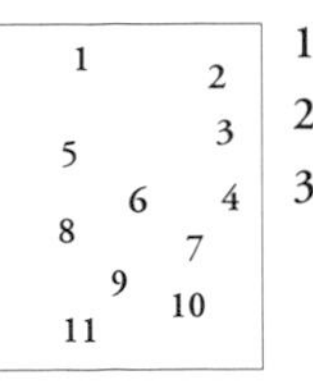

1. Open Mouth Routers
2. 9½ins. T&G Combination Plane
3. No.8 Swinging Fence Matching Plane
4. 22ins. Buck Panel Plane
5. ⅜ins. Side Bead
6. No.7 ½ins. Side Bead
7. ⅜ins. Side Bead
8. No.5 Square Oval
9. No.8 Hollow
10. No.4 Side Bead
11. No.3 Hollow

14IN RAZZE JACK PLANE

William Marples & Sons

1938

The term 'Razze' Jack is of American origin and identifies technical planes of this sort where the stock is reduced in depth towards the heel. It resembles the Pattern Makers Plane on page 24. Jack planes are much used bench planes. The iron is ground very slightly convex to stop the edges digging in and the tool is used for preparing surfaces for a trying plane, jointer or smoother. This Razze Jack cost 8/- in 1938!

28IN TRYING PLANE

Shaw & Co., Arthington, Manchester

C.1810

Trying planes are traditionally between 22ins. and 28ins. in length. The closed handle offset to the right was phased out after about 1820. The 2¾ins. cap iron was supplied by G. T. Hildick, London; 1823-1824. Trying planes are used to produce straight matching edges for jointing two boards together – or producing a flat surface.

7½IN COFFIN SMOOTHER

Moseley & Son

1819-1830

Coffin smoothers are short smoothing planes approximately 8ins. long and coffin shaped. This one has an I. & H. Sorby iron dated circa 1840. Moseley & Son were in New Street, Covent Garden, London, from 1819-1830.

3½IN MODEL MAKERS PLANE

Early 20th Century

The smallest plane currently in the collection, measuring 3½ins. x 1ins. It has a single iron and an alloy body.

7½IN NORRIS A5 SMOOTHING PLANE

1948

A Norris A5 smoothing plane complete with invoice from Hammond & Hussey Ltd., 23-25 High Street, Croydon; dated 25 September 1948 and retailing at £3.17.6d. A well made and highly thought of plane having a cast steel body with stained hardwood infill, brass screwed lever cap and screw adjusted 2ins. iron. Shown with original box.

1
2 4
3
a 5

1. 7½ins. Norris A5 Smoothing Plane
2. 7½ins. Moseley Coffin Smoother
3. 14ins. Razze Jack Plane
4. 28ins. Trying Plane, Shaw & Co
5. 3½ins. Model Makers Plane

a. 12ins. 3-Fold Boxwood & Brass Ironmongers Rule with brass caliper

STANLEY NO.1 SMOOTH PLANE

Late 19th Century

The No.1 Smooth Plane is a mere 5¾ins. long with a 1¼ins. iron, used for final adjustments.

STANLEY NO.2 SMOOTH PLANE

Late 19th Century

The No.2 is a general purpose bench plane; 7ins. long with a 1⅝ins. iron.

STANLEY NO.3 SMOOTH PLANE

Late 19th Century

The No.3 is also a general bench plane, though a little longer at 8ins. with a 1¾ins. iron.

All three series smooth planes, developed from Bailey's designs, are made of cast iron and have a rosewood handle and knob. Though nearly 100 years old, they epitomise the American approach to modern mass produced planes which were beginning to dispense with a wood infill in the body work.

12IN PATTERN MAKERS PLANE WITH INTERCHANGEABLE CURVED SOLES & IRONS

C.1890

A set of five soles with five irons which can be quickly interchanged. Each 1¾ins. iron is matched to a curved sole which locks onto the base of the plane by a screw fitting into a keyhole slot. These were used to shape wooden patterns for sand moulds. The soles are marked in sizes and the irons supplied by Ward, J. Gleave & Sons of Manchester and John Redlich, 6 Syre Street, Sheffield.

DOVETAILED STEEL RABBET PLANE

Stewart Spiers of Ayr

C.1900

Although this is a contemporary of the Stanley planes above, it shows the 'metal frame' tradition with a wood infill continuing in U.K. planes. Spiers of Ayr had been making significant developments in metal plane designs since the mid 1840s. The steel frame is dovetailed to a steel sole and has a rosewood infill. Two ¾ins. irons by Ward are set in tandem and held with rosewood wedges.

1
2
5
3
4

1. 12ins. Pattern Makers Plane, Curved Soles & Irons
2. Stanley No.3 Smooth Plane
3. Stanley No.1 Smooth Plane
4. Dovetailed Steel Rabbet Plane, Spiers of Ayr
5. Stanley No.2 Smooth Plane

AUSTRIAN COMPASS PLANE

1834

A small wooden Austrian compass plane with carved date 1834.

TOOTHING PLANE

Early 20th Century

A toothing plane has a fine toothed iron for preparing surfaces for veneering.

SET OF 4 ROUNDERS

Early 20th Century

The set comprises four sizes, ⅝ins., ¾ins., ⅞ins. and 1ins. A length of wood is prepared to a slightly oversize octagon and the rounder is spun round it producing a correct sized dowel. Larger rounders were used for turning broom handles.

SELF CENTERING PLOUGH

Early 20th Century

The self-adjusting and self-centering mechanism between the two fences is similar to that found on parallel rules. Beechwood, with an ebony wedge.

STOP CHAMFER PLANE

C.1905

An unusual beechwood stop chamfer plane by Joseph Buck. Chamfer planes are open mouthed to give the user good blade visibility.

NO.30 BAILEY JOINTER

Late 19th Century

The Bailey 22ins. Jointer has a 2⅜ins. double iron and lever cap in a casting which is screwed to the wooden stock. The lever cap is made by Stanley, New Britain, Connecticut, U.S.A. It is marked Sargent & Co. No.3422. One of the most interesting planes in the collection, for it shows the evolving transition from wood to metal planes.

Leonard Bailey made great contributions to the development of the plane between 1858 and 1869. He sold his business and patent rights to the Stanley Rule & Level Co., joined them and produced the 'Bailey Adjustable' plane designs in 1870.

1	2	
1		1
	1	3
4	5	
6		a

1. Set of 4 Rounders
2. N0.30 Bailey Jointer
3. Austrian Compass Plane
4. Stop Chamfer Plane
5. Toothing Plane
6. Self Centering Plough

a. 24ins. 2-Fold Brass Rule

17in Norris A71 Jack Plane

Early 20th Century

The A71 Pattern is a 17ins. beechwood jack plane with the Norris improved screw iron adjustment.

Steel Dovetailed Mitre Plane

Isaac Sorby

C.1900

By 1900, planes of this construction can be regarded as very traditional having derived from the open mitre box planes of the early 19th Century. The steel body frame is dovetailed together over a rosewood infill. The snecked iron (i.e. hooked or nibbed so that the blade can be eased back with a hammer) is fixed in position with a rosewood wedge.

Irish Pattern Chariot Plane

T.S. Kaye & Son

Late 19th Century

T.S. Kaye & Son were based in Hull. The "Irish Pattern" has a 1¾ins. iron with a carved wooden infill.

Chariot Plane

Isaac Sorby

C.1900

An Isaac Sorby chariot plane with an iron compassed sole.

4in Toy Plane

Early 19th Century

A 4ins. wooden 'toy' small plane with a 1ins. single iron, used by a piano maker at Bromley in Kent.

14½in Beechwood Jack

Buck

Mid 19th Century

A jack plane in beechwood with a 2½ins. Ward iron and removable side fillet. Removal of the fillet enabled it to be used for rebate work.

This tool relates to a period of partnership (1838-1852) at Tottenham Court Road, London, between George and Joseph Buck, during which their tools were stamped Buck.

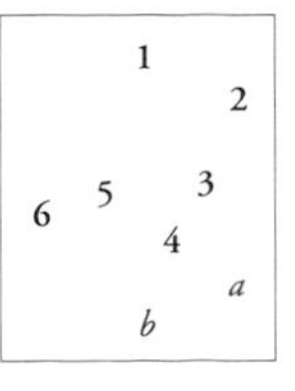

1. 17ins. Norris A71 Jack Plane
2. 14½ins. Beechwood Jack
3. Chariot Plane, Isaac Sorby
4. 4ins. Toy Plane
5. Steel Dovetailed Mitre Plane
6. Irish Pattern Chariot Plane

a. Pair of Ivory & Brass Parallel Rules
b. 4ins. Boxwood & Brass Level marked in 1ins. and ⅛ins. divisions

A selection of the many braces, Ultimatum, plated and plain, in the Toolbank Museum

Tools for Boring

THE TOOLBANK COLLECTION

Bevel gears; French hand drill

Chairmaker's pad

An Ultimatum brace; detail

Revolving tools made an early appearance in man's history and went through many stages before evolving into the precise cutting instruments of today. The first major transformation, spanning thousands of years, was from bone splinters and pointed flint blades (abrading), to copper awls and then Iron Age forms of 'spoon' bit or auger (cutting). The effectiveness of these tools was limited by the twisting motion of the wrist, or by working hand over hand for a few turns only, before rotation had to be reversed to clear parings.

Before the advent of nails, almost everything had to be fitted with wooden dowels or lashed together with leather thongs or rope. As augers and drills improved they became indispensable tools in all forms of construction and eased the work of making mortices.

The central problem is to obtain continuous rotation with a bit holder that can withstand the turning strain. The alternatives are either to use a low speed of rotation with high torque (boring), or to use a high speed with relatively low torque (drilling).

Flywheel on a pump drill

The faster bow drill, traceable to the early Egyptians 4,500 years ago, and the Roman pump drill are recognisable antecedents though they were only capable of small diameters. The familiar brace and bit of medieval origin afforded continuous motion, but the inherent weakness of its cranked construction limited its use to drilling pilot holes for larger auger bits. Wooden braces were progressively strengthened with metal into the early 20th Century, despite the earlier introduction of iron sweep braces.

The idea of inserting a spindle and bevel gearing across the cranked area of an iron brace and applying a drive handle (circa 1820) enabled drill speeds to exceed the rotational speed of the handle. Milling machines were introduced in the 1860s, which could cut a twist mechanically instead of hand filing. The combination of these two factors meant that the brace and the bit could finally 'come of age' as the modern hand drill.

Of all the basic types of tool to be invented, those for boring or drilling took the longest to mature.

ANGLE BORING MACHINE
C.1900

This Angle Boring Machine was found in a warehouse in Glasgow. Its purpose is to bore vertical or angled holes in heavy ship or wharf timbers. The machine is laid on the timber and one sits astride a platform to hold it firmly in place. A locking bolt across the two semi-circular side plates ensures any selected angle remains fixed. The auger spindle is self-feeding and powered by turning the double crank. Once the hole has been bored, a sliding cog is engaged on the left hand rack. The spindle will then withdraw with continued turning of the crank. When fully retracted a clip engages to retain the spindle.

FRENCH BEVEL GEAR DRILL
C.1890

Earliest examples of this type of bevel gear drill probably date from the end of the 18th Century. It is clearly a forerunner of today's hand drills. Although having only a single pinion gear, it is nevertheless able to deliver faster rotational speeds than the traditional carpenter's brace. There is no chuck in the modern sense. A tapered bit is held in a drive socket. Early hand drills lack a side handle, but the shaft is thicker above the gear drive to provide better grip for the user.

RAWLPLUG HAMMER DRILL
C.1930

An early design of an hand powered hammer drill patented by Rawlplug, No.338.884, papers for which were filed on 21 August 1929. Rotation of the handle turns the drill and also activates a spring loaded hammer within the framework.

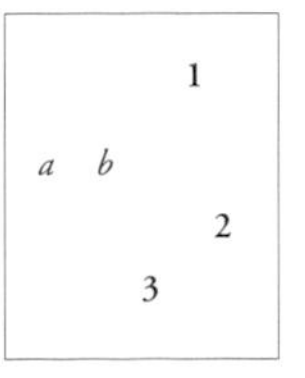

1. Angle Boring Machine
2. French Bevel Gear Drill
3. Rawlplug Hammer Drill

a. Miller Falls Right Angle Drill
b. Beechwood Channel Spill Plane

TOOLS FOR BORING

THE TOOLBANK COLLECTION

MILLER FALLS HAND DRILL

C.1900

The small Miller Falls Hand Drill is a very basic drill with a pin chuck.

MILLER FALLS BREAST DRILL

C.1900

A large breast drill by Miller Falls which incorporates a useful spirit level.

MASONS BOW DRILL

C.1880

A mason's bow drill by G. Buck, Tottenham Court Road, London. This version is in steel, lignum and brass.

MASONS DRILL BOW

C.1880

The bow is used in conjunction with a mason's bow drill and has a sprung steel blade (similar to a fencing foil). There is a ratchet adjustment in the bow handle to adjust to the correct tension. The cord is wrapped once round the drum section of the drill and 'bowed' from side to side to produce the rotary movement. Several types of bow are available, from simple wooden ones to the more sophisticated spring foil type.

SCOTCH PATTERN AUGERS

Late 19th Century

A set of 3 traditional pattern augers for boring holes in timber. A bar is put through the ring at the top to form a handle.

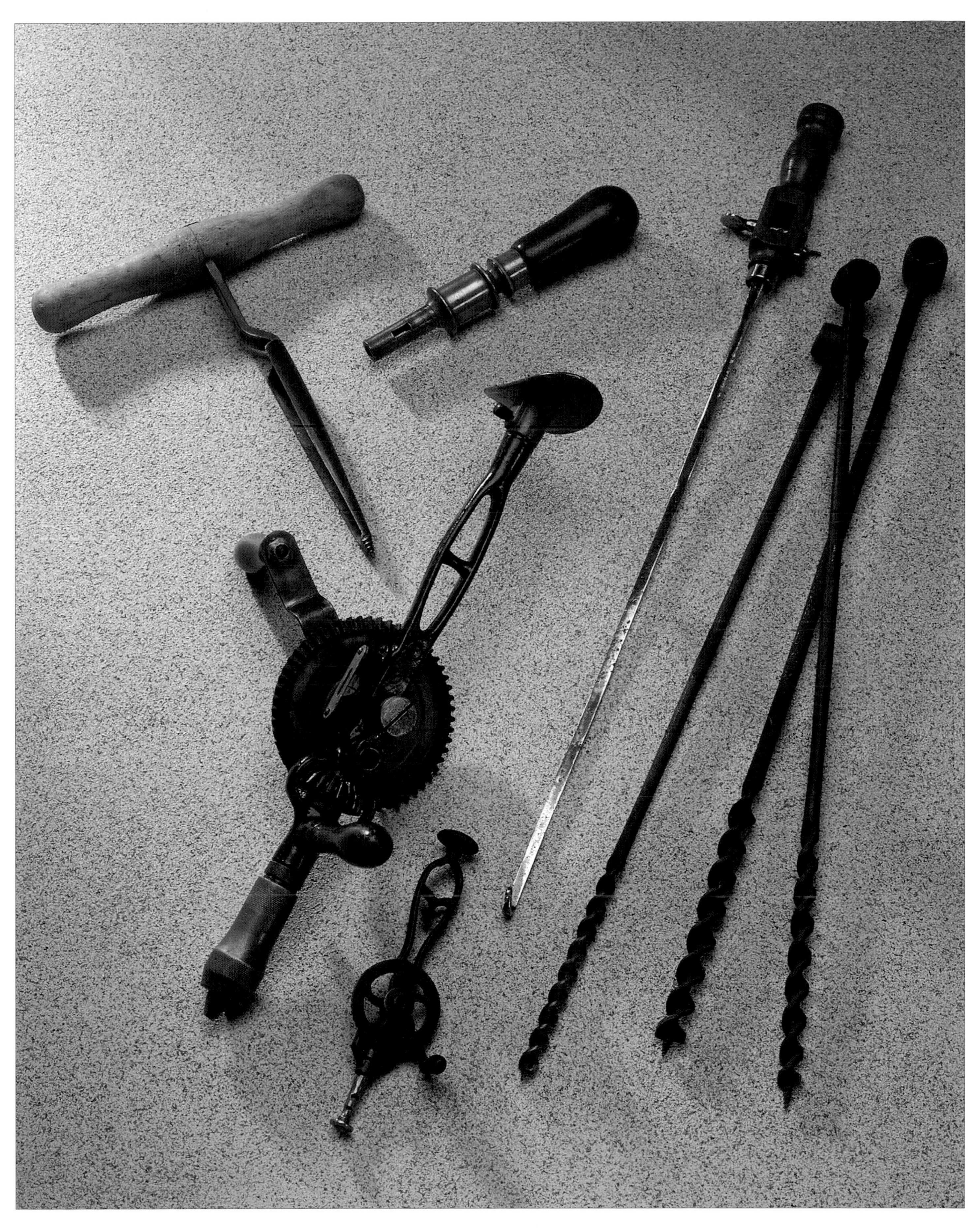

1 2 a 3 5 4

1. MASONS BOW DRILL
2. MASONS DRILL BOW
3. SCOTCH PATTERN AUGERS
4. MILLER FALLS HAND DRILL
5. MILLER FALLS BREAST DRILL

a. Ladder Makers 14ins. Auger, I. Sorby

Tools for Boring

THE TOOLBANK COLLECTION

Chairmakers Beechwood Brace

Late 19th Century

A late 19th Century form of today's interchangeable tool sets enabling the chairmaker to accomplish many tasks with the one tool. The brace has seven different bits, known as pads, which can be inserted into a square-shafted, brass ferruled lever chuck.

Pump Drill

Late 19th Century

This is fundamentally a Stone Age tool, the only refinements being a flywheel of brass instead of stone and a cord instead of a leather thong to generate rotation. It is remarkable that in Europe such a very old design proved perfectly adequate for small work, such as watchmaking etc. until the beginning of this century. In other parts of the world it remains in common use.

Scotch Pattern Iron Brace

Thomas Ibbotson

Late 19th Century

A simple iron brace with lever chuck and a hardwood and brass head.

Sixpenny Brace

Late 19th Century

An early French steel and boxwood sixpenny brace. The penny worth was the price charged in 1900.

Armourers Brace

Early 20th Century

This 'ladies'' brace was used by armourers in the early part of this century and was made of brass for safety reasons – to avoid causing sparks!

Ultimatum Brace

William Marples

C.1880

Perhaps the Ultimatum can be regarded as the zenith of this form of brace. The brass reinforcing frame on this superb example adds to its looks as much as its strength. It has an ebony infill and head, and is fitted with a taper chuck.

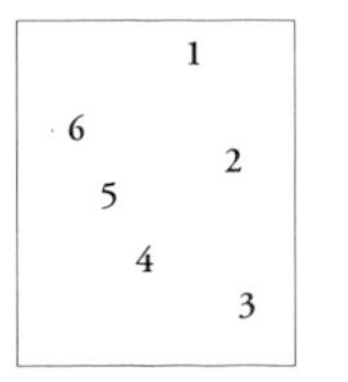

1. Chairmakers Beechwood Brace with 7 pads
2. Scotch Pattern Iron Brace, Thomas Ibbotson
3. Pump Drill
4. Armourers Brace
5. Sixpenny Brace
6. Ultimatum Brace, William Marples

Tools for Boring

Gas Fitters Brace

Briggs Wall & Co.

Late 19th Century

Pattern C263 was the code given to this spare but pleasing all steel design. Drill bits are locked into the stock by a side nut.

Plated Brace

Robert Marples

C.1840

Made at Robert Marples' Hermitage Works, Sheffield. A beechwood frame, reinforced with inlaid brass plating, and an ebony revolving head.

Plain Brace

J. Buck

1850-1860

The Plain Brace has a simple wooden frame, revolving head and single brass button chuck.

Ultimatum Brace

Buck

Mid 19th Century

The brass framed Buck Ultimatum Brace was made as a 'presentation' brace of cast brass and ebony, patented by William Marples around 1850-1860. It features a revolving handle, head and brass chuck. A cheaper version was made in beechwood. So few beechwood ones have survived that they are now more valuable than the presentation braces!

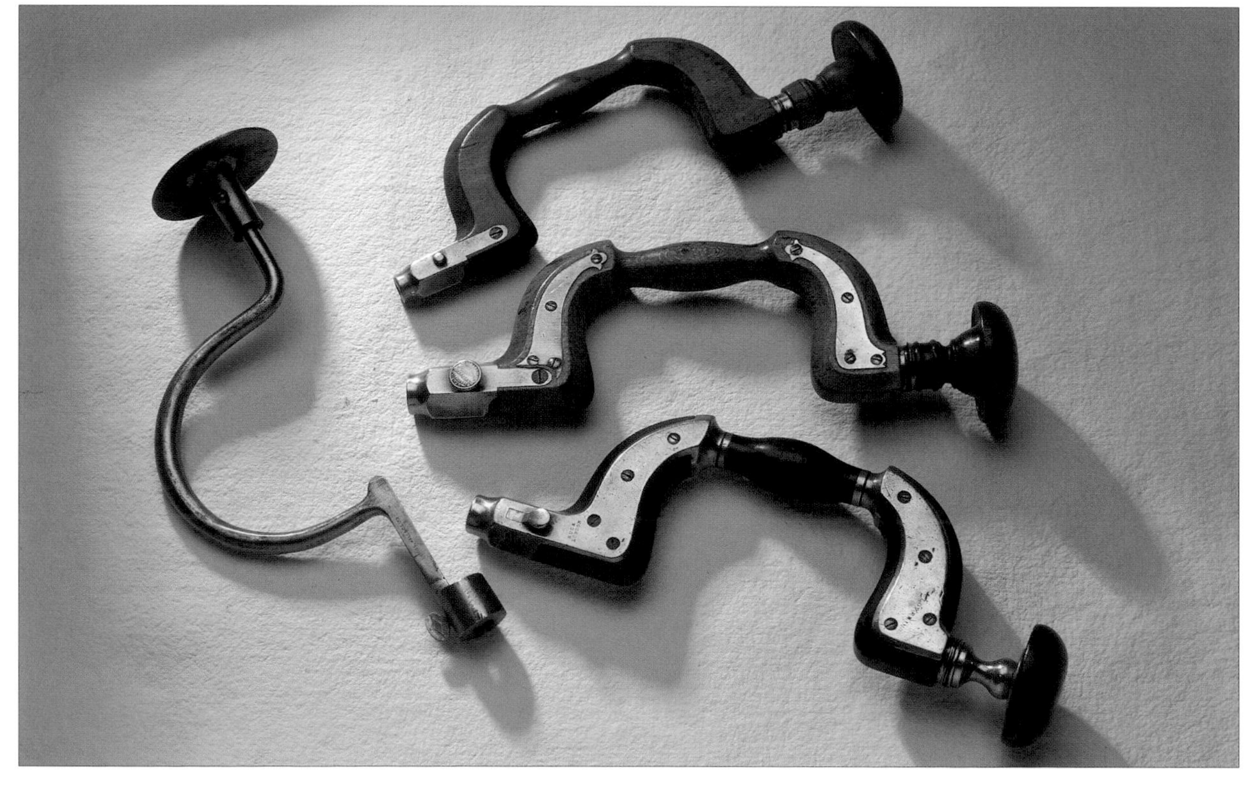

1
2
4 3

1. Plain Brace, J. Buck
2. Plated Brace, Robert Marples
3. Ultimatum Brace, Buck
4. Gas Fitters Brace, Briggs Wall & Co.

Coopers & Wheelwrights Tools

THE TOOLBANK COLLECTION

Croze; detail of cutter

Brace and bit; detail

Traveller; detail showing notch

In terms of packaging and storage, the cask was a huge advance on skins, gourds or earthenware jars. Pliny the Elder believed that cask making originated in the alpine valleys. Julius Caesar described the making of military bridges using casks as floating platforms. In the Old Testament circa 9th Century BC, Elijah the Prophet defeated the priests of Baal after filling four barrels with water and pouring them on the burnt offering (1 Kings xviii 33). Remember also that Diogenes the Cynic (d. 324BC) dwelt for many years in a tub!

The presence of coopering as a trade in England is recorded in 1298AD when a number of coopers were fined! The Coopers' Guild received its first Charter in 1501 and built the halls of the Company in Basinghall Street, London, on land bequeathed by John Baker, a Guild member.

Cask types were either tight ('wet'), or slack ('dry'). The latter could be made with softwood. Tight casks demanded the greatest skill and craftsmanship, as some fermenting liquids could reach pressures of 30-40psi.

Bung hole borer and reamer; leading thread and cutter

Moreover, the size had to be correct and there was a working relationship between coopers and the trades which sold a cask's contents to given measures. Coopers' skills gave rise to the many specialised tools you see here.

The wheelwrights' trade has an equally long history stretching back five millennia and continues to this day. The art lies in making wheels 'dished' so that the spokes taking the weight remain at right angles to the ground. There have been several advantages to this discovery. A dished wheel keeps the hub bearing against the axle collar, away from collets and nuts. It withstands side jolts better, and allows the wagon floor to be widened without widening the axle. As the 19th Century drew to a close, mechanical aids like the Automatic Spoke Lathe and the Spoke Tenoning & Throating Machine were beginning to modernise wheelwrights' ways.

Coopering, however, remained the hand craft it had always been until the coming of new container materials.

COOPERS TRAVELLER

Early 19th Century

The Traveller is a prime example of a user made tool. Its purpose is to measure circumferences on hoops etc. and does the job of a tape measure. Note how the metal disc has been notched for counting the number of revolutions. Even the handle has been thoughtfully angled for convenient use.

SUN PLANE

J.G. Maddin

Mid 19th Century

Sun Plane by J.G. Maddin, 204 St John Street, Clerkernwell, London; also called a topping plane. After the staves have been trimmed with an adze, the sun plane smoothes the tops of the staves to provide a level surface to take the fences of the shiv or croze.

COOPERS SHIV

Mid 19th Century

The Shiv (or Chiv) is a type of plane. Before the croze is applied for cutting the groove, a shiv must first be run round the inside staves to form a smooth even surface. By running the fence along the top of the cask and pushing outwards, the plane iron can pare off any uneven excess.

COOPERS CROZE OR CHEVE

Mid 19th Century

The Croze is a specialist tool designed to be run round the inside of the cask at top and bottom, to cut a groove which will receive the barrel-head or bottom of the cask.

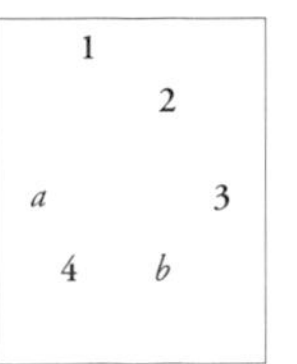

1. Coopers Croze or Cheve
2. Coopers Shiv
3. Sun Plane, J.G. Maddin
4. Coopers Traveller

a. Coopers Adze
b. Bung Borer

Wheelwrights Bruzz

Mid 19th Century

A heavy 'V' shaped chisel to cut out mortice corners, for example spoke mortices.

Wooden Taper Auger

Late 19th Century

Otherwise known as a bung borer. A tapered wooden stock with a long spokeshave type iron.

French Coopers Swift

C.1900

Mainly used for smoothing heads of casks.

Double Handed Scorpe

1885

Used for shaving the inside jointing between staves. This one has been marked with the date 1.6.85.

Single Handed Scorpe

Late 19th Century

Similar to the double handed scorpe; used to level the inside of staves.

3in Skew Adze

Late 19th Century

Hand forged with a skew edge. Locally made by a blacksmith.

1. French Coopers Swift
2. 3ins. Skew Adze
3. Wheelwrights Bruzz
4. Single Handed Scorpe
5. Double Handed Scorpe
6. Wooden Taper Auger

a. No.1 Cast Iron Glue Pot with lid
b. Square with Plumb Bob, forerunner of the spirit level

COOPERS BRACE AND BIT

Mid 19th Century

A plain beechwood cooper's brace with fixed spoon bit, which is used to drill holes in edges of boards so that they will take dowels when making up the cask head.

NAILING AND HOOPING ADZE

Mid 19th Century

For driving and fixing hoops in position.

BELLY KNIFE

Buck

C.1850

For hollowing the inside of staves. The blade is made of 'electro-boracic steel' – a long discontinued process of treating and making steel using cyanide!

CURVED DRAWING KNIFE

Wm. Langley & Co.

C.1900

A drawing knife by Wm. Langley & Co. with curved blade, often used for smoothing or finishing surfaces after axe work.

HOOP DRIVER

C.1900

A hand made driving hammer with handle, for placing or removing barrel hoops.

COOPERS JIGGER

Read

C.1900

A cooper's jigger by Read. Used mainly in repair work where the correct size shiv is not available. Held from the outside, the forged end is used inside the cask to work like a shiv, smoothing the inside surface in preparation for the croze.

FLAGGING IRON

C.1900

Coopers used the Flagging Iron mainly in repair work, to force staves apart and to assist with injecting 'flags' or rushes to seal joints between the staves.

COOPERS SIDE AXE

William Greaves

C.1900

A William Greaves side axe. The blade on a side axe is ground on one side only to give a controlled cut. It was generally used by coopers for trimming staves and rough shaping cask heads.

1. Coopers Brace and Bit
2. Hoop Driver
3. Coopers Side Axe, Greaves
4. Flagging Iron
5. Curved Drawing Knife, Langley
6. Belly Knife, Buck
7. Coopers Jigger, Read
8. Nailing and Hooping Adze

a. Brass Folding Square

Riveting Bits, 1/4in and 5/16in

Mid 19th Century

A hole is punched at each end of the hoop and a soft iron rivet inserted into one of them. The two ends of the hoop are then drawn together. The hole in the bit (punch) is placed over the rivet to keep it in place and force both ends of the hoop together. Finally, the domed end punch is used to secure the rivet.

Bung Hole Borer and Reamer

Mid 19th Century

For inserting taper plugs or taps to casks which will contain liquids. The auger twist at the end starts off the bore hole, which is widened gradually by a reamer up the side of the taper.

Stave Jointer or Long Jointer

T.F. Gardner, Bristol

Early 20th Century

A stave or long jointer 64ins. in length with a 3ins. single iron complete with leg stool. Made by T.F. Gardner of Bristol, 1899-1939, with iron by I. & H. Sorby, 1824-1881, it is like a large jack plane supported at an angle by a leg stool. The iron faces upwards. Coopers use it to fashion the correct stave angle and width for the diameter of the cask being made. In addition, the correct taper top and bottom must be produced to give the cask its characteristic barrel shape (i.e. having a smaller diameter at either end relative to the diameter across the middle). The wooden stave is pushed downwards against the cutter.

1
2
3

1. Stave Jointer or Long Jointer, T.F. Gardner
2. Riveting Bits
3. Bung Hole Borer and Reamer

Shipwrights Tools

THE TOOLBANK COLLECTION

Scull plane; iron made from a cut down firmer chisel

Shipwright's caulking mallet; detail

Caulking chisel by Ward

Boat building tools have been found in Viking Age graves, and a complete tool chest was found in the famous Mastermyr long boat in Gotland. The picture we gain from medieval artists, and from tools recovered from Henry VIII's flag ship Mary Rose suggests that shipwrights' tools remained largely unchanged for a thousand years.

Toe end of a mast plane

For the most part, the ancient world favoured 'carvel' built boats (where the 'strakes' or hull planks are abutted side by side). The Viking tradition opted for 'clinker' built hulls (where the strakes overlap).

Despite the simplicity of their tools, early shipwrights must be congratulated on building such beautiful and daring craft. Shipbuilding has always required a high degree of order and method.

Shipwrights developed some very complex carpentry for forming a keel into a bow stem or stern post, by 'scarfing' the joints. Other techniques were devised for curving beams and for inlaying reducing numbers of planks towards the ship's stem. Fastening of planks was done with 'trenels' ('treenails') cleft from oak in lengths varying from 12-36ins. and shaped with a drawing knife into octagon cross-sections of 1¼-2ins. The skill of the caulker ensured the overall structure stayed watertight. (In many respects the skills of shipwright and cooper are similar and may have developed concurrently in the ancient world).

Construction techniques remained largely unchanged well into the 18th Century with most ships weighing around 100-350 tons. Diagonal framing techniques introduced in the English Navy after 1770 permitted increases in size and tonnages beyond 500 tons.

The launching of Brunel's visionary first iron hull ship Great Britain in July 1843 may have presaged the changes that would occur to the shipwrights' trade, but it required another 40 years' experimentation with 'Ironclad' hulls (and then steel from about 1880) for progress to be made in that direction. In the meantime Clipper ships ruled the waves. Commercial barque rigged ships remained popular at the end of the 19th Century, and keels for wooden hulled merchant steamers were still being laid up to the 1914-1918 war.

Aboard wooden vessels the position of ship's carpenter was always very important. With simple tools he could ensure that his ship was well tended and seaworthy.

CAULKING CHISELS

C.1820

A selection of caulking chisels. The correct size chisel must be used with a caulking mallet to firm oakum into the spaces between deck planking so that it lies just below the surface. The oakum is then sealed over with hot pitch.

DECK DOWELLING BITS

C.1830

A selection of deck dowelling bits. Heavy ship's decking was bolted down. The plank is bored with say a ⅜ins. hole. A dowelling bit with a ⅜ins. plug nose (behind which is a centre bit of approximately 1ins to 1¼ins diameter) is inserted in the hole and drilled to sufficient depth to take both the bolt head and a wood plug or dowel on top to seal the hole.

SCULL MAKING PLANE

C.1900

User made by a shipwright. A small 6ins. version of a compass plane with a convex sole and an iron adapted from a cut down 1½ins. firmer chisel. It would have been used for forming the hollowed out sections of scull blades. (Other examples of compass planes are shown on pages 18 and 26).

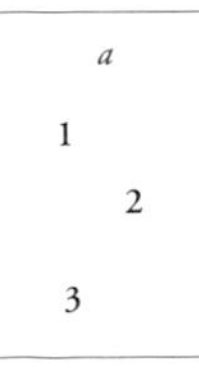

1. Deck Dowelling Bits
2. Scull Making Plane
3. Caulking Chisels

a. *Pin Pol Adze*

Shipwrights Tools

THE TOOLBANK COLLECTION

Spar Planes

Spar planes are so called because they are used to prepare masts, spars and sail booms etc. They are similar in appearance to coffin smoothers (such as the Moseley coffin smoother on page 22) and have soles with matching irons that are concave, in various diameters to create the taper of the mast.

8½in Mahogany Single Iron Spar Plane
I. Sorby
1810

8in Beechwood No.6 Spar Plane
A. Mathieson & Son, Glasgow
C.1860

7in Beechwood Spar Plane
W. Dibb, York
C.1820

7in Beechwood Spar Plane
W. Gilpin
C.1870

Caulking Mallet
C.1850

A caulking mallet is used for driving caulking chisels, shown on the previous page. Hardwood with metal bound faces.

	2	
1		3
		4
5		

1. 8½ins. Sorby Single Iron Spar Plane
2. 7ins. Dibb Spar Plane
3. 7ins. Gilpin Spar Plane
4. 8ins. Mathieson No. 6 Spar Plane
5. Caulking Mallet

Measuring & Marking

THE TOOLBANK COLLECTION

Forester's axe; showing the coat of arms

Blind man's rule; Braille markings detail

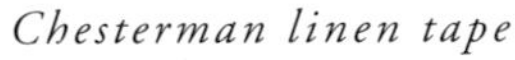

Chesterman linen tape

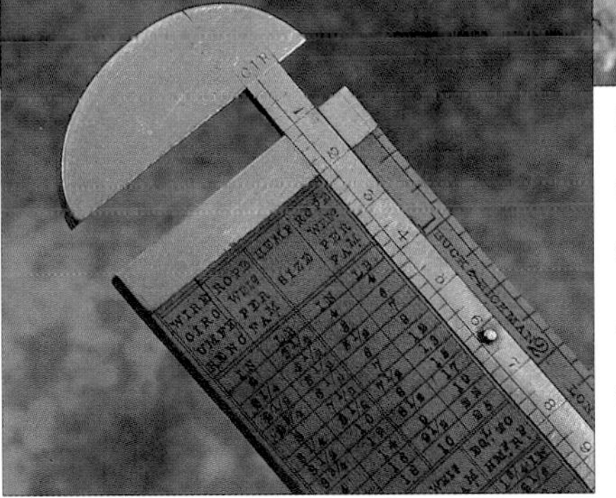

Rope and chain gauge

It was trade, building and navigation which propelled the evolution of measuring devices. Sundials, compasses, clocks and scales helped to make these activities more reliable and efficient. To appreciate the legendary accuracy of the Great Pyramid of Gisa, or of what remains of Stonehenge, is to realise how essential measurement has been to civilisation.

A standard of measurement may be based on almost anything, provided it is accepted by all concerned. The Indus Valley peoples used the Mina, Kus and Ka which were derived from personal physical attributes. The Egyptian Cubit became an ubiquitous standard, but complicated sub-divisions constrained its augmentation in the wider world. Rome adopted a mixture of systems and introduced Unciae ("Inches") as well as the Libra ("Pound"). Thereafter, many customary weights and measures satisfied local needs for almost a thousand years.

A standard, however created, must satisfy two criteria; that of accuracy, where the value of a measured quantity is correct in relation to the laid down standard; and that of precision, where any number of measurements of the same quantity will yield the same results. Societies have had to strike a balance between an optimum level of accuracy and the cost of achieving it.

Gabrielle Mouton's radically different concept in 1670 sought some universal attribute – he proposed a unit of length based on one minute of an arc of a great circle of the earth – and a consistent decimal base. The idea grew into the French 'metric system' laid down in 1799, which became adopted in 35 countries by the beginning of the 20th Century.

The scientific requirement to include electro-magnetism and light within this system of absolute relationships took years to solve, with invaluable work being done by Coulomb, Maxwell and Oersted. The world now has a sound theoretical measuring base (SI Units, adopted in 1960) to cope equally with the sub-atomic and the galactic.

Whereas axes, saws and planes appear to have reached a plateau in their development, it is certain that the quest for more accurate and precise measuring tools has a great deal further to go. Some everyday tools have already adopted laser and acoustic distancing techniques. The measuring and marking tools on the next few pages were used during this significant revolution from customary measures to metrication.

36in Tailors Straight Trouser Stick

John Rabone & Son

20th Century

Tailor's rule, No.1516 in boxwood with a bevel edge.

45in Tailors Straight Trouser Stick

John Rabone & Son

20th Century

Tailor's rule, No.1517 in boxwood with a bevel edge.

Tailors Fixed Square

John Rabone & Son

20th Century

Tailor's Fixed Square, No.1507, 12 x 24ins. in brass and boxwood.

Scribes for marking logs and timbers

Estate Foresters Marking Axe

19th Century

A rare tool in this country. The blade of the axe is used for clearing an area of bark on a standing tree intended for felling. The face opposite the blade has a set of initials or coat of arms cut into it. This is stamped onto the tree as an identification mark.

Fine Brass and Ebony Mortice Gauge

C.1900

Exquisitely crafted. There is an 8ins. rule along the handle in 1/16ins. divisions.

a
1 2
3 4
5

1. 45ins. Tailors Straight Trouser Stick, Rabone
2. Tailors Fixed Square, Rabone
3. 36ins. Tailors Straight Trouser Stick, Rabone
4. Fine Brass and Ebony Mortice Gauge
5. Estate Foresters Marking Axe

a. Pair of Side Rebate Planes

SCRIBES FOR MARKING LOGS AND TIMBERS

SWAN NECKED DRAG KNIFE

Early 20th Century

Ex Port of London Authority timber scribe.

TIMBER SCRIBE

Late 19th Century

Shaped octagonal hardwood handle had a point with cutter to inscribe circles and fixed drag knife. French made.

FOLDING DRAG KNIFE

Late 19th Century

A point with cutter to inscribe circles. The knife is marked with the Government broad arrow.

24IN BOOKBINDERS RULE

Kelly & Sons

20th Century

Kelly & Sons were at Arundel Street, London.

66FT LINEN TAPE MEASURE

John Rabone & Son

Mid 19th Century

This old example of a linen tape measure in a leather case was kindly donated by David Prosser. The tape length indicates it was a surveyor's tape for land measurement; 66 feet being 1 chain (or 100 links), which is an eightieth of a mile – or even the length of a cricket pitch!

2 3 1 5 4

1. Swan Necked Drag Knife
2. Timber Scribe
3. Folding Drag Knife
4. 66ft. Linen Tape Measure, Rabone
5. 24ins. Bookbinders Rule, Kelly & Sons

CALIPERS

19th Century

Simple blacksmith made calipers for measuring logs.

6IN IVORY RULE

J. Rabone & Sons

Early 20th Century

Two fold ivory rule with subdivisions in sixteenths of an inch.

ROPE AND CHAIN GAUGE

Buck & Hickman

Early 20th Century

From Buck & Hickman catalogue No.5452. Boxwood with nickel-silver fittings.

50FT LINEN TAPE MEASURE

Chesterman

C.1895-1905

This example of a linen tape measure in a brass and composition case was kindly donated by Harry Westropp, Managing Director of Rabone & Chesterman.

a 1
b
2
4 3

1. Calipers
2. 50ft. Linen Tape Measure, Chesterman
3. Rope and Chain Gauge, Buck & Hickman
4. 6ins. 2-Fold Ivory Rule, Rabone

a. Iron Rebate Plane with rosewood infill
b. Brass Headed Bossing Mallet with cane handle

Brass Trammels

C.1900

Trammels as illustrated are used for describing large sweeps and circles etc. Also known as compass beams, they consist of a wooden, or metal, beam and two sliding bevels again either of wood or metal, which can be secured in required positions with a screw or wedge. The heads may have a point or a pencil. The Brass Trammel (No.2) has circular fretwork.

Blind Mans Rule

J. Rabone & Sons

20th Century

Rabone's No.1167 boxwood and brass, 24ins. 4-fold rule has Braille markings on it which have been made up using small dome headed pins. Very large lettering has been used to help the partially sighted.

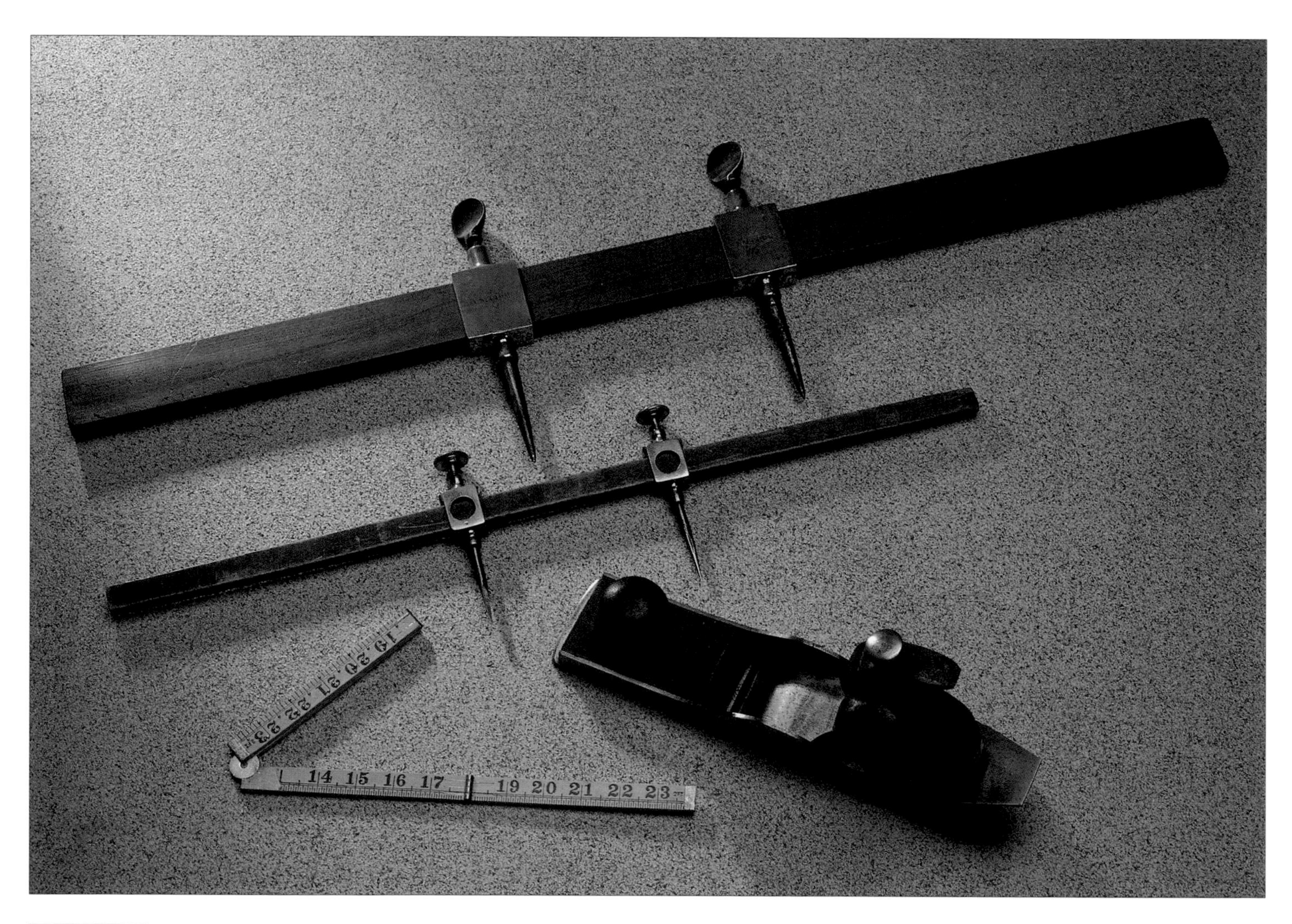

1
2
a
3

1. Engraved Brass Trammel
2. Brass Trammel
3. Blind Mans Rule

a. 12½ins. Low Angle Steel Plane with 2⅜ins. iron

LEATHER WORKERS TOOLS

THE TOOLBANK COLLECTION

Saddle maker's pricker

Blanchard saddler's plough plane; detail

Punch; showing size, name and trademark

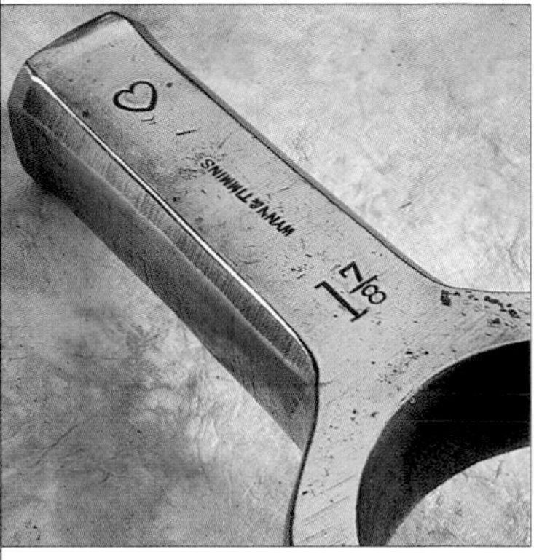

Hand wheel pricker

The presence of so many synthetic materials today can obscure the vital part that leather continues to play in daily life, as it has done since the great period of animal domestication 7,000 years ago. The ancient Egyptians and Hebrews were working leather on an industrial scale by then, though the Saharan and Arctic peoples already had a reputation for excellent craftsmanship. Among the earliest objects uncovered from ancient times are sandals, bags and cushions constructed of leather. In later times, it was used for making armour, boats, water skins and buckles. The Moors were masters of saddle making, and Spanish leatherwork became fashionable in the 16th and 17th Centuries.

Leather is one of the strongest flexible sheets known and will resist tearing and puncturing. It absorbs, breathes, insulates and can be stretched, wrapped, folded, stamped and carved. It can be punched and drilled, and seams will hold when sewn.

Before leather can be worked creatively it must undergo four curing stages to remove hair and excess tissue before becoming sufficiently soft and supple; a process which used to take one to two years, but which now takes about 14 days. Traditional tanning was with alum or a mixture of aldehydes, oils and vegetable tannins such as oak and chestnut wood. Modern curing processes use chrome tanning or vegetable tanning.

Leather played an extremely important part in the invention of books, once it was found that leather could be thinly sliced or skived. The visual traditions of surface modelling, or 'bossing' the leather, live on in modern book design.

Supply, however, was traditionally controlled at a local level by the demand for meat, so hides have traded internationally as a commodity for a long time in order to meet fluctuations in the market. By the early 19th Century there was a great diversity of leather working trades, and new ones were being created to meet the needs of steam power, particularly for drive belts and seals to hydraulic pumps.

Leather Workers Tools

Saddle Makers Prickers
Early 20th Century

Leather punches like this are made in a variety of sizes and are used to indent the skin so that stitching will not be proud of the surface.

"Bulldog" Lasting Pincers
Early 20th Century

A shoemaker's tool for stretching leather over the last.

Leather Workers Hand Wheel Pricker
Early 20th Century

The spiked wheel is used to step the position of stitch holes.

Saddlers Plough Plane
Blanchard of Paris
C.1860

Brass and steel with a rosewood handle. Leather workers used a plough plane to cut leather into strips. The fence is adjustable and has a metric scale. The Parisian leather making quarter was traditionally centred around the 11th and 12th arrondissements.

Single and Double Leather Workers Creasers
Early 20th Century

Both examples are German. Creasers can be used hot or cold to form decorative lines or creases in leather, typically around the edges of a belt.

Leather Workers Punches
Wynn & Timmins
C.1900

A splendid set of polished steel large punches for leather etc. Sizes are 3ins., 2ins., 1⅞ins., 1¾ins. and 1⅝ins.

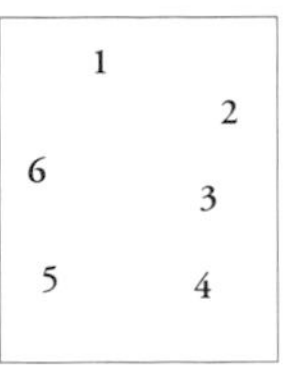

1. Leather Workers Punches, Wynn & Timmins
2. "Bulldog" Lasting Pincers
3. Saddlers Plough Plane, Blanchard
4. Saddle Makers Prickers
5. Leather Workers Hand Wheel Pricker
6. Single and Double Leather Workers Creasers

Ornate casting of clinometer;
Davis Level & Tool Co. U.S.A.

LEVELS

THE TOOLBANK COLLECTION

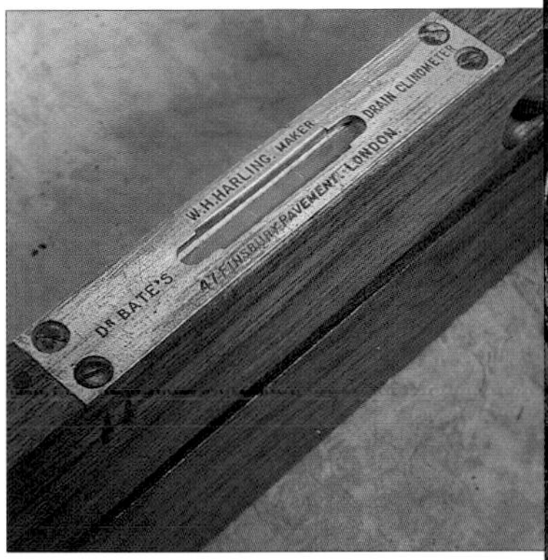

Davis clinometer; detail

Dr Bates drain clinometer; engraving detail

"Climax" iron spirit level; detail

German clinometer; engraving detail

Another aspect of measurement is that of ensuring that work is properly horizontal (i.e. 'level') or vertical (i.e. 'plumb'). For that matter, any other angle or plane that is not either level or plumb needs to be describable and measurable.

As we would expect, there have been effective ways of achieving this, using squares, levels or compasses, though they remained rudimentary for centuries. Sparse archaeological evidence of these tools must be inferred from funerary reliefs, medieval paintings and illustrations. The simplest form of level is made up of three pieces of wood joined together to make an 'A' frame with a line and lead weight suspended from the apex. ('Plumb' line is derived from the Roman word for the metal 'plumbum', meaning lead).

The ancient world was well aware that "water finds its own level" and Hero of Alexandria is reputed to have made a level consisting of two glass cylinders filled with water and connected by a tube; a modern equivalent is still useful today to lay drainage and guttering or suspend ceilings, for example. The Roman architect Vitruvius devised an arrangement of plumb bobs which floated in an open water trough – called the Chorobates. It was cumbersome, but he was evidently thinking along the right lines! Another interesting approach, during the 17th Century, was to suspend a simplified form of astrolabe, onto which was clamped a sighting piece at 90° to its vertical diameter. This produced a horizontal line of sight.

A forerunner of the spirit level can be traced back to the Italian astronomer Riccioli who, in 1630, obtained a more precise 'horizontal' necessary for his observations by using a glass tube with upturned ends, filled with water. Melchisédech Thévenot's invention of the bubble level, in about 1665, was the significant breakthrough. The straight tubes of early models resulted in erratic bubble movement, which was cured either by slightly arching the tube, or grinding the interior surface to an arc. Bubble levels, telescopic sights and tripods were generally well established by 1700.

The spirit level or clinometer, as early levels were called, is the main focus of interest in this type of tool within The Toolbank Collection.

Levels

THE TOOLBANK COLLECTION

Clinometer
German origin
Late 19th Century

A beautifully made pocket-size clinometer with a rotating arm spirit level, which lays across a viewing aperture and can be read off against a scale. Shown with its original presentation box.

Clinometer
Davis Level & Tool Co. U.S.A.
Late 19th Century

A virtuoso mixture of precision and delight in decoration. This 18ins. cast iron Davis Clinometer has milled edges. The central spirit vial will set plumb and level, and is also adjustable as an angle setter.

Railway Level
Alex Marshall of Glasgow
C.1900

Plumb and level glass vials are set in a hardwood stock, which is inlaid on three sides by precision metal faces. An interesting feature is the peep hole and through siting line just above the long edge.

Brass Plumb Bob and Reel
C.1880

A traditional and little changed style of plumb bob, for obtaining an accurate upright position. The steel point is spring loaded to prevent damage if dropped.

Dr Bates Drain Clinometer
W.H. Haring
C.1900

Made by W.H. Haring, 47 Finsbury Pavement, London. The wooden level, hinged at one end, can be elevated with an adjusting screw and the inclination read off against a scale.

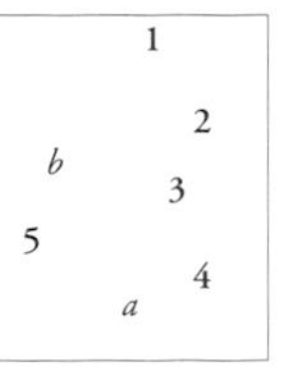

1. Dr Bates Drain Clinometer, W.H. Haring
2. Inclinometer, German origin
3. Inclinometer, Davis
4. Brass Plumb Bob and Reel
5. Railway Level, Alex Marshall

a. 6ins. Steel & Brass Level
b. 8ins. "Climax" Iron Spirit Level
Both a. & b.: J. Rabone & Sons

Levels

9in Round End Spirit Level

J. Rabone & Sons

Mid 19th Century

Ebony and brass construction. There is a sliding double blind to protect the level vial when not in use.

9in Boat Level

J. Rabone & Sons

Mid 19th Century

A tapered end level listed as product number 1625 in a Rabone catalogue. It has vials for both plumb and level.

4in Spirit Level

Mid 19th Century

These 4ins tropical hardwood levels were sold by W. Preston of Pentonville, London, though the original manufacturer is unknown.

1. 9ins. Round End Spirit Level, J. Rabone & Sons
2. 4ins. Spirit Level, sold by W. Preston
3. 9ins. Boat Level, J. Rabone & Sons

a. 33ft. Plasticon Tape, in a Bakelite case marked Hockley Abbey, J. Rabone & Sons
b. Frenzelit Tape in a Bakelite case, Rudolf Frenzel, Germany. Blade made in England

CHISELS & AXES

THE TOOLBANK COLLECTION

Carving chisels

French goosewing side axe; stamp detail

London Pattern side axe; stamp detail

Butt seating cutting machine; detail

We may regard the axe as the original multi-purpose tool. Certainly it is the second longest serving tool in human history after the 'hammerstone'. From a time 200,000 years ago when tools were hardly distinguishable by their uses, and, whether as a weapon, or for digging, scraping or chopping, the axe-like implement made of bone or worked stone was held directly in the hand.

The critical step 35,000 years ago was hafting, or the fitting of a handle. This gave the axe an extended radius and sufficient kinetic energy with which to fell trees, opening the way to deforestation for agriculture. The polished neolithic axe head, together with the flint adze and chisel, became the tool kit that turned wood into an almost universal building material. All three tools showed a gradual development during the maturation of the Bronze and Iron Ages between 6400BC to 1100BC, though the discovery of both metals required the support of many other inventions, such as kilns, casting and tempering to allow them to be fully exploited for toolmaking.

Initially, the scarcity of metals and the difficulties in working them meant that bronze and iron were used primarily for military, ornamental and ceremonial purposes before being put to use in the manufacture of agricultural or building implements. The hafted metal axe could resist 'twist' when wedged in a cut. Metal chisels would, crucially, become 'secondary tools' in the making of other tool products.

During the Middle Ages the axe became the most useful of all tools with four common shapes for felling and preparing timber. Local variations in pattern proliferated throughout Europe well into the 19th Century, but their overall importance was already declining as a result of increasing efficiency in hand and later machine sawing.

The many 18th and 19th Century chisels and axes in the Toolbank Museum are illustrative of the variety found in different trades. Two prized pieces, the Goosewing Side Axe and the Twybill, or Besaigue, are both 18th Century and of French origin.

Lock Mortice Chisel
Buck

Colloquially known as a 'gooseneck mortice chisel' by its shape. The old style mortice locks had rounded ends. These chisels were used to scoop out the round ends of the mortice.

All Steel Lock Mortice Chisel
Mid 19th Century

Unfortunately, no maker's name can be attributed to this all steel version.

French Twybill or Besaigue
18th Century

Here is a tool that is not a whit different from its forbears illustrated in 15th Century woodcuts and is sometimes referred to as a 'mortice axe'. It is mainly used for forming mortices in large framing timbers, for houses and barns. The main bulk of the mortice must be cut and removed with an auger. The twybill's chisel edge is used to cut the sides; the opposite end, which is shaped like a mortice chisel, is then used to extract the chippings.

Scribing Gouge
C.1860

For sash work. The extended wooden handle acts as a stop when used with a template for jointing sash bars.

French Carpenters Axe
Early 19th Century

A broad asymmetrical blade that tapers on the underside. Blades of this shape became commonplace during the Middle Ages.

French Splitting Axe
C.1880

Another familiar pattern, of medieval origin. Today's splitting axes have a less exaggerated taper.

London Pattern Side Axe
Ward

1824-1859

The 'side' or broad axe is used for squaring or shaping beams and planks. The blade is ground on one side only, and the handle is offset to protect fingers during use.

French Goosewing Side Axe
C.1750

The French Goosewing Side Axe is the oldest tool in The Toolbank Collection and still in remarkably good condition. A hard steel cutting edge has been forge welded onto the softer iron blade. An obvious crack is beginning to appear along the join due to past wear and tear.

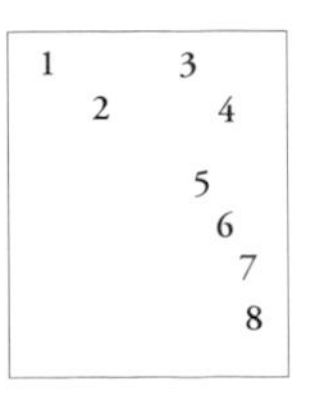

1. French Carpenters Axe
2. London Pattern Side Axe, Ward
3. French Twybill or Besaigue
4. French Splitting Axe
5. French Goosewing Side Axe
6. All Steel Lock Mortice Chisel
7. Lock Mortice Chisel, Buck
8. Scribing Gouge

HINGE OR BUTT SEATING CUTTING MACHINE
Waller Tool Co., Chicago
C.1890

This ingenious device cramps onto door jambs. Using the ratchet handled lever, a bottom knife and side cutters cut the bottom and sides of the hinge recess. The other short linkage at the base of the big lever is used to force down a vertical cutter, completing the last cut and removing the whole piece of surplus wood.

HAND OPERATED MORTICE MACHINE
1898

Timber is cramped to a movable bed that can be advanced either forwards or backwards, or side to side by means of hand wheels. Various sizes of chisel can be pre-fitted. The chisel is forced down by lever action of the handle, and withdrawal is assisted by a counterweight. Powerful machines like this were very popular in timber yards to mortice oak fence posts. This model is date stamped 1898.

1 | 2

1. HINGE OR BUTT SEATING CUTTING MACHINE, WALLER TOOL CO.
2. HAND OPERATED MORTICE MACHINE

SPANNERS & WRENCHES

THE TOOLBANK COLLECTION

Front screw wrench; detail

Terry's turbine spanner; detail and part of Patent Office papers

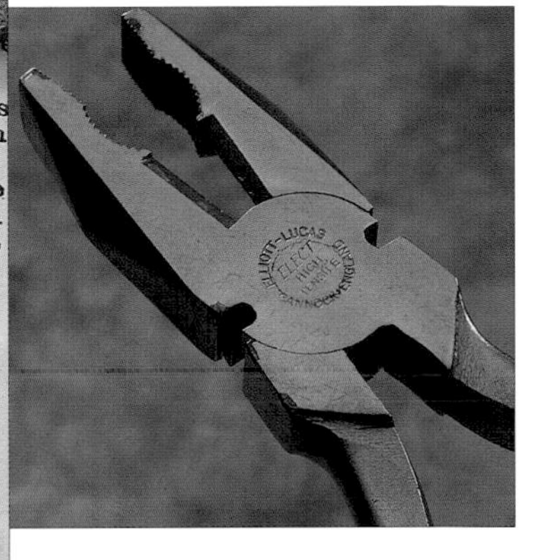

Elliott Lucas 'Electeloy' pliers; detail

Ibbott improved rapid adjusting spanner; detail and part of Patent Office papers

Wrenches are a recent innovation in terms of tool history. Their function is to turn or torsion a threaded nut or bolt in order that two materials can be firmly held together.

There is no certain date at which wrenches began to be used, though it is likely to be around the 15th Century when Europe embarked on its first stage of industrialisation, to convert water power (by waterwheels) and wind power (using windmills) into usable mechanical energy.

The common jointing methods of the period such as mortices, treenails and nails could never have coped with the mechanical stresses that were required to be harnessed.

Early spanners and wrenches were simple but effective smith made tools. The double ended cart wrench in the picture on page 88 is typical of this genre and is likely to have been as standard a tool for the millwright as for the wheelwright.

The 18th Century ushered in a rapid expansion of the small toolmaker's craft as industrialisation forced the pace of invention. Harder metals and closer tolerances were being exploited to make lathes and boring mills. As a consequence, there was a demand for better quality tools with which to do the job.

The adjustable hammer wrench shown on page 73, sometimes called a 'screw hammer', is a factory made forerunner of today's hand wrenches. Other types of wrench were tooth jawed and cleverly exploited the turning moment about a fulcrum in order to increase grip, the harder the wrench was closed. Modern examples of this type of wrench are pipe wrenches and the Stillson. A design like the Ibbott improved rapid adjusting spanner shown on page 73 sought to combine simplicity of construction with a minimum of moving parts.

For wrenches that rely solely on muscle power, today's designs have probably reached a plateau of development. But, in the search for power greater than this, new forms of hydraulic and electro-pneumatic wrench are still being created.

Adjustable Hammer Wrench

C.1850

An altogether more purposeful design than the Terry's Turbine Spanner below. The centre screw adjustable thread allows fine adjustment and there is plenty of jaw capacity available from the remaining thread within the handle. There is a possible weak point along the moving jaw where it bends to form a collar around the handle. The hammer face has not been case hardened and has become rather worn.

Front Screw Wrench

1897

Stamped 7 September '97. The movable jaw has 'twin bars' into the handle, presumably for strength and rigidity. Only one of the 'bars' is threaded to take the knurled adjuster nut. Part of the handle is heavily ridged to help hand grip.

Ibbott Improved Rapid Adjusting Spanner

A.R. Ibbott

C.1932

The Improved Rapid Adjusting Spanner by A.R. Ibbott was patented by Burston and has complete and copiously annotated patent papers which received acceptance on 8 December 1932. Patent No.384.468. The papers are shown on page 89. A rotating cam is used to adjust and hold the position of the movable jaw.

Terrys Turbine Spanner

Albert V. Terry, Redditch

C.1910

A detail of the patent papers accepted on 1 December 1910, patent No.7671/10, can be seen on the previous page. The drawings and specifications were very thorough and illustrate the principle of adding or subtracting hinged 'fingers' to change jaw width. It is doubtful whether the idea was either practicable or successful! The Terry's Turbine Spanner was kindly donated by Andy Andrews.

1
4 2
3
a
b

1. Adjustable Hammer Wrench
2. Front Screw Wrench
3. Terrys Turbine Spanner
4. Ibbott Improved Rapid Adjusting Spanner

a. Elliott Lucas "Electeloy" Wire Strippers, 1951
b. Elliott Lucas "Electeloy" pliers, made for Rolls Royce, 1950

Stanley manufactured a Universal Combination Plane known as the '55' between 1897 and 1963, and sold it under the banner "A planing mill unto itself". The model shown here, which is circa 1920, boasts 53 cutters and not one (as on a '55'), but two fences, pivot and tilt, for chamfering – making it a '55E'.

An Amalgam of Tools & Small Machines

THE TOOLBANK COLLECTION

'Mikado' bicycle spoke threader; detail

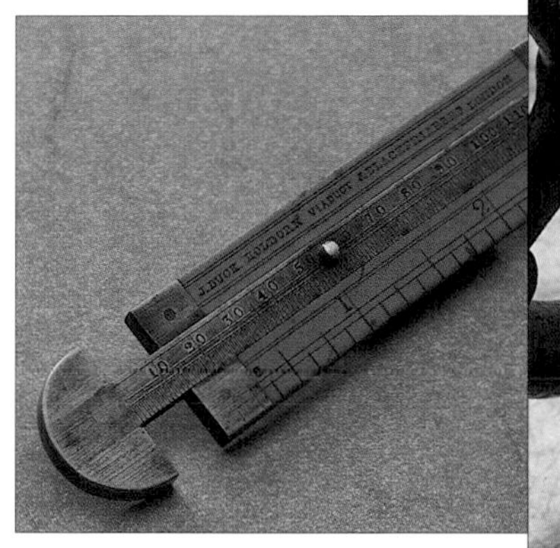

Button gauge with 40 divisions to the inch

Watch mainspring winder; detail

These pages take a discursive look at the many other interesting and unusual tools in The Toolbank Collection. They illustrate the remarkable 'propagating power' of tools. New forms are developed to solve a particular problem. But not only is there a tendency towards specialisation as people find new uses for them, but also the fact that a tool, once made, makes possible the construction of a still better one. Small machines are shown too. They are hand powered but pose the question "When does a hand tool become a machine?"

McCormick mower blade grinder; detail

The seeds of this overlap go back to the 18th Century when tools of a machine scale were being invented. Maritz is credited with the boring mill in 1713. By 1770 Verbruggen had made an improved machine for boring cannon. Vaucanson and Senot both devised lathes between 1775 and 1795. These machines could make other machines.

In that century the tool making tradition had grown upon the skills of individuals themselves, like the 'Little Mesters' of Sheffield. But their methods of production were increasingly out of kilter with those who sought to solve bigger engineering problems – who needed better and more specialised tools and whose own methods of working already required a workshop or factory style basis of production. A crucial step was made by Benjamin Huntsman, a clockmaker, who perfected the making of crucible steel in 1746 and began producing it commercially by 1751. Here at last was an extremely hard metal, strong enough to cut other metals, with which the toolmaker could respond.

Man's rate of material progress has been determined by his tools. It is these extensions of the hand that lead to automation.

Men like Verbruggen, Vaucanson and Senot were unwitting originators of a process of 'building the skill into the tool' to overcome human error. Reduced error has been bought by the loss of versatility of tools, since they are employed at their most efficient when used in the mass production process. The skill of the individual versus mass production was the underlying controversy of the Industrial Revolution. Ultimately it was the skilled craftsmen who themselves drove that revolution in their pursuit of more exacting and higher standards of workmanship and the need to find novel solutions to production problems.

ORNAMENTAL PLASTERERS MOULDING TOOLS

Early 20th Century

A variety of brass moulding tools – fifteen in all – for the ornamental plasterer. Some of the smaller ones can be used to create repeat patterns and borders.

OLD WORN SCYTHE

Mid 19th Century

This old scythe has seen some hard work in its lifetime. The wavy edge is caused by sharpening stones wearing away the softer parts, due to uneven tempering.

JOINERS WOODEN TOOL CHEST

C.1912

The tool chest of the late Mr Street gives us a fascinating glimpse into his lifelong job as a joiner. The chest holds 69 tools that were his stock in trade. There are rules, marking gauges, shaves, chisels, gouges, rebate planes and a wooden frame saw. One of the tenon saws has been resharpened and reset so often that the blade is scarcely more than two inches deep!

Mr Street's tool chest is very utilitarian in comparison to the Seaton Chest on display at the Rochester Museum, Kent. Both serve to illustrate that there was a long tradition of joiners and carpenters making their own tool chests for the workplace. Some tradesmen built very ornate work inside a plain looking tool chest as a form of 'curriculum vitae' to show what they were capable of doing. One suspects that Mr Street had no need to promote himself in this way and was always in work.

1. OLD WORN SCYTHE

1

	3
2	

2. Joiners Wooden Tool Chest of the late Mr H.J. Street
3. Ornamental Plasterers Moulding Tools

Progressively, throughout the last century and with even greater impetus in this century, there has been a drive to create mechanical solutions to tasks done by hand. The first two examples below were made to these ends. Both are useful tools, albeit for very specific tasks.

SUPER CUTAWL MINOR JIGSAW

C.1936

The Super Cutawl Minor Jigsaw is a power tool for cutting patterns in cardboard, wallboard, softwood and paper etc. The original design has been improved to make this a very important forerunner of the jigsaws we use in industries today. The details on the circular plate are: Type B11, Serial No.1371, Supertools Ltd., 351 High Street, Chiswick, London. Patent No.465.535, papers for which had been filed on 11 January 1936. The equipment includes several spare accessory packets of saws and chisels.

MOWER BLADE GRINDER

McCormick

C.1900

A hand powered bench grinder for triangular bladed cutter bars on mowing machines. The blade is firmly cramped on a hinged mechanism that moves in and out. The revolving stone oscillates up and down against the blade. Made by McCormick, U.S.A.

OAK WITCHETT

T. Turner, Sheffield

1844-1868

This witchett has brass jaws and is adjustable to create different diameters, unlike the rounders on page 27 which are of fixed sizes. The witchett is spun round a length of wood, brought roughly to size with a drawing knife, and produces a round section like a broomstick. Made by T. Turner, 35 Queen Street, Sheffield 1846-1868; the iron, by Reamley & Wood, Sheffield, is circa 1860.

1	
	2
3	*a*

1. Mower Blade Grinder, McCormick
2. Super Cutawl Minor Jigsaw
3. Oak Witchett, Turner

a. 14ins. Steel Dovetailed Panel Plane

An Amalgam of Tools & Small Machines

THE TOOLBANK COLLECTION

Watch Mainspring Winder

Late 19th Century

A manufactured tool for work on pocket watches. Kindly donated by relatives of the late Mr R.W. Clifford.

Veterinary Firing Iron

C.1920

For treating strained leg tendons of horses. The practice is now mercifully outlawed. The iron was heated red hot and a series of sears applied, about ¾ins. apart, across the skin overlaying the tendon.

French Cider Sampler

Late 19th Century

This elegantly designed tool works as a gimlet and a tap. The steel stem is hollow, with a curved spout and tap at one end and a gimlet at the other. There are two fine perforations in the stem just above the gimlet thread. Once the threaded end has been screwed into a wooden cask, driven from the handle – a cider sample can be drawn off through the spout!

'Mikado' Bicycle Spoke Threader

Late 19th Century

A hand threading 'lathe' for putting threads on bicycle spokes. It consists of a cramp which faces a threading die on a spindle and a bearing, turned by a cranked wheel. A spoke is first cut to length and cramped in position. The spindle has a fore and aft play of about an inch, so that when the die has engaged, it becomes self-feeding.

Syers Pattern Bench Knife Vice

C.1900

Two steel pegs on the bottom of the vice are located in a series of holes in a bench top. The piece of wood to be planed is trapped between a bench stop and the arm of the vice, which is then tightened by the lever. Kindly donated by Stephen Gratwick.

User Made Scraper

Early 19th Century

Entirely fashioned by the user and made with a piece of blade from a handsaw. The scraper is used to produce a finish on wood, to eliminate marks and deal with difficult grain. The edge of the steel plate has been turned slightly with a hard steel burnisher. The resultant burr takes off a fine shaving.

1 2 3 6 5 4 a b	1. User Made Scraper 2. Veterinary Firing Iron 3. Syers Pattern Bench Knife Vice	4. French Cider Sampler 5. Watch Mainspring Winder 6. 'Mikado' Bicycle Spoke Threader	*a. No.40 Cast Iron Glue Pot, E. Pugh & Co.* *b. Washer Cutter, Wynn & Timmins*

Plumbers Dummy
C.1910

Plumbers Dummy with a lead head and cane handle. The dummy is inserted into misshapen lead pipes or vessels and acts as an 'anvil' to reshape the pipe when it is dressed from the outside.

Scaffolders Hammer
C.1920

A scaffolder's hammer, with axe head and a hammer nail extractor. Essential in the days when scaffolding was built using wooden poles and ties. The ties were of galvanised soft wire combined with twists of hemp.

Plumbers Bossing Mallet
C.1900

A quality tool which has lignum vitae for the head and a lancewood handle.

Scratch Stock
C.1920

User made Scratch Stock. A simple tool of wood and steel, where the steel plate is filed to match a moulding profile and used to scrape small runs of the moulding.

Beechwood and Brass Shave
McKeand of Manchester

C.1830

Many contemporary shave tools of the period would still have been hand made by the user. This very pleasing design in beechwood and brass was manufactured by McKeand of Manchester.

Violin Makers Cramp
Late 19th Century

Cramps are used in quantity when gluing up the top and bottom faces of a violin to the sides. They are spaced very closely around the edge.

Flower Gathering Scissors
Lilleyman of Sheffield

C.1900

Scissors, 6½ins. long, with leather pads to hold the stalk.
Made by Lilleyman, 12 Edward Street, Sheffield.

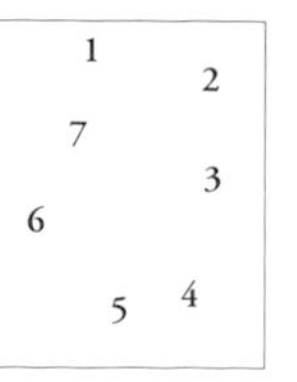

1. Beechwood and Brass Shave, McKeand
2. Scratch Stock
3. Flower Gathering Scissors, Lilleyman
4. Scaffolders Hammer
5. Plumbers Dummy
6. Violin Makers Cramp
7. Plumbers Bossing Mallet

2IN BEECHWOOD SCREW BOX WITH STEEL TAP

Late 19th Century

3/16IN BOXWOOD SCREW BOX WITH METAL TAP

J. Buck

C.1900

Screw boxes are made in two parts with a steel 'V' shaped cutter to cut a thread, fixed in one part. The boxes can be separated to enable the cutter to be removed and sharpened. For sizes above 2ins. the taps are generally made from a wooden rod with a metal tooth to cut the thread. Metal taps have a square section at the top so that a key can be fitted and turned like an auger. Wooden taps have a cross bar.

1 / 1 / 2

1. 2INS. BEECHWOOD SCREW BOX WITH STEEL TAP
2. 3/16INS. BOXWOOD SCREW BOX WITH METAL TAP, J. BUCK

Hammers, Screwdrivers & Turnscrews

THE TOOLBANK COLLECTION

French slater's masette; detail

Silversmith's repoussé hammer; detail

Spear & Jackson turnscrew; detail

Cabinet maker's turnscrew; shaft detail

If one is asked to "think of a tool" the likely answer that comes first to mind is "a hammer", of which the most familiar is probably the adze-eye claw hammer of American origin, otherwise known as the carpenter's claw hammer. No other group of tools has quite such powerful and deep seated imagery associated with it. In the Old Norse legends, Thor's weapon was a hammer. A 'martel-de-fer' or 'iron hammer' was a Dark Age weapon which had at one end a pick and at the other a hammer: Charles Martel earned his epithet having led the Franks to victory over the Saracen invaders of Gaul in 732AD. The expression is used when goods are sold at auction, or when parties are negotiating hard to conclude a deal.

The hammer was in effect Man's first tool, profoundly changing his way of life. Therein may lie the significance of its imagery deep in our language. The pounding implement or 'hammerstone' was fitted at some time with a handle to increase the blow and put to use as a miner's maul in flint and copper mines.

Today's familiar hammer shape was already established in Roman times. The hammer was used alongside the wooden mallet. The proliferation of hammer styles since the Middle Ages recalls the wide range of specialisations found in plough planes, and arises out of frequent adaptations to an often used tool. Styles have, interestingly, tended to be named after towns, for instance 'Warrington' or 'London', whereas axe styles have been given county names like 'Kent' or 'Suffolk'.

In complete contrast to the hammer's ancient lineage, the screwdriver, or turnscrew as it was called in the middle and north of England, may be only quite recent. The Greeks, as usual, had the theory first – the screw thread is attributed to the Pythagorean philosopher Archytas of Tarentum (8th Century BC). Wooden screws were used in Roman times in wine and olive presses. But early evidence of metal screws and screwdrivers is inconclusive until the publication of Agricola's De Re Metallica in 1566, in which only the screw is illustrated. The earliest clear reference for the actual named tool is in Nicholsons Mechanical Exercises (London; J. Taylor, 1812).

French Metalworkers Hammer

C.1890

Joiners Bench Hammer

Timmins & Sons

C.1890

Silversmiths Repoussé Hammer

C.1900

Watchmakers Small Hammer

C.1900

London Pattern Turnscrew

C.1900

27½ins. long.

Cabinet Makers Turnscrew

C.1900

'Cabinet maker's Pattern' 26½ins. long with oak handle.

Turnscrew

Spear & Jackson

1948

Registered pattern 611.274 with cross oval boxwood handle and plated ends.

b 1 2 / a 3 / 5 / 7 6 4	1. Cabinet Makers Turnscrew 2. London Pattern Turnscrew 3. French Metalworkers Hammer 4. Turnscrew, Spear & Jackson	5. Joiners Bench Hammer, Timmins & Sons 6. Watchmakers Small Hammer 7. Silversmiths Repoussé Hammer	*a. French Slaters Masette* *b. Brass and Gunmetal Smoothing Plane*

The Toolbank Museum

THE TOOLBANK COLLECTION

The tools that have been presented in this book are but a small cross section of those to be seen in the Toolbank Museum which now number more than 850 items – and are still growing. Wally Flude, the curator, has devoted more than 10 years to gather a collection of this size. Each item is identified, dated where possible and logged with a short description.

Approximately 90% of the collection, spanning tools of all trades, is made up of British tools that are factory made, more often than not in the Sheffield area, or are self made by the skilled hands of the user. The rest are of American or European origin, some of the rarest being 18th Century French.

Tools are gradually being acquired by purchase or donation. One of the most recent additions is the Union Lathe on the page opposite and currently undergoing restoration is the Fiddle Seed Spreader! Tool selection is made on the basis of what is interesting or has unusual qualities and has seen real practical use, rather than seeking out those tools valued by the antique market. The Toolbank Museum now has a large number of printing blocks of illustrated tools from old catalogues.

What is strikingly evident is that well made tools, even when well used, do nevertheless last a very long time.

a. Rectangular Die Stock with ¼ins. die
b. French Curved Bladed, Right Handed Side Axe, stamped Gros Narbonne
c. 36ins. Steel Tape by Chesterman. Inches, in London Standard, measure the diameter, and read off the circumference
d. Double Ended Cart Wrench
e. Laboratory Gas Pliers, Wynn & Timmins

An old workbench showing the many tools used in the shipwrights' trade

Foot pedal operated Union Lathe, used for wood turning

A selection of the many back saws in the Toolbank Museum

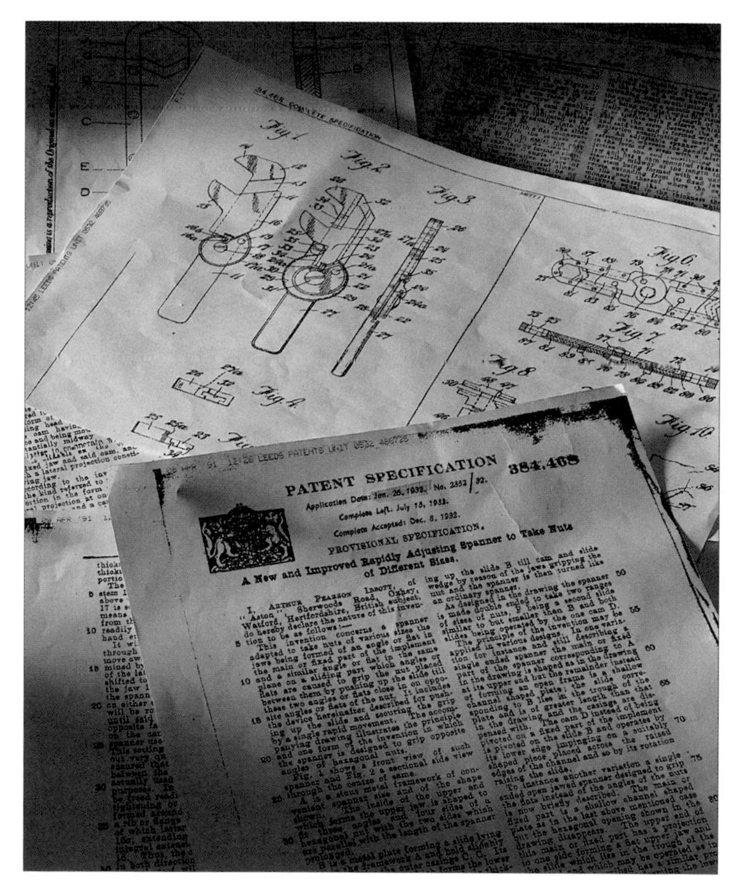

Patent Office papers. Specification drawings relating to the Ibbott Improved Rapid Adjusting Spanner.

Early catalogues play an invaluable role in the Toolbank Museum. They have helped to identify and date many of the tools, and are also a record of evolving ideas in tool design.

BIBLIOGRAPHY

Abell, W. (1948)
The Shipwrights Trade,
Cambridge: University Press Cambridge.

Bunch, B. and Hellemans, A. (1993)
Timetables of Technology,
New York: Simon & Schuster.

Daumas, M. (1980 translated E.B.Hennessy)
History of the Invention of Technology,
London: John Murray.

Eckington, G. (1933)
The Coopers Company & Craft,
London: Sampson Low, Marston & Co. Ltd.

Encyclopaedia Americana (1991)
Danbury: Grolier Incorporated.

Evans, H.T. (1970 second edition revised)
The Woodworkers Book of Facts,
London: The Technical Press.

Greenhill, B. (1980)
The Ship: The Life and Death of the Merchant Sailing Ship 1815-1965,
London: Her Majesty's Stationery Office.

Greenhill, B. (1976)
Archaeology of the Boat,
London: A. & C. Black Limited.

Goodman, W.L. (1964)
The History of Woodworking Tools,
London: G. Bell & Sons Ltd.

Goodman, W.L. (1968)
British Plane Makers from 1700,
London: G. Bell & Sons Ltd.

Jackson, A. and Day, D. (1978)
The Complete Book of Tools,
London: Michael Joseph Limited.

McGowan, A. (1980)
The Ship: The Century Before Steam
The development of the sailing ship 1700-1820,
London: Her Majesty's Stationery Office.

Phillipson, J. (1897)
The Art and Craft of Coach Building,
London: G. Bell & Sons.

Rolt, L.T.C. (1986 revised)
Tools for the Job A History of Machine Tools to 1950,
London: Her Majesty's Stationery Office.

Salaman, R.A. (1986)
Dictionary of Leatherworking Tools c.1700-1950
and the tools of allied trades,
London: George Allen & Unwin.

Salaman, R.A. (1989 revised)
Dictionary of Woodworking Tools c.1700-1970
and the tools of allied trades,
London: Unwin Hyman Ltd.

Smith, D.J.M. (1988)
Dictionary of Horse-Drawn Vehicles,
London: J.A. Allen & Co. Ltd.

The New Encyclopaedia Britannica (15th edition)
Chicago: Encyclopaedia Britannica Inc.

Vince, J. (1975)
An Illustrated History of Carts and Wagons,
Bourne End: Spurbooks Ltd.

Index

Adzes 41-44, 49
Angle Boring Machine 32
Atkins 12
Augers 34-35, 42
Axes 44, 51-52, 67-68, 88
Bailey, Leonard 15, 24, 26
Banthel, G. ii
Bicycle Spoke Threader 75, 80
Blanchard 59-60
Blow Lamp ii
Brace Pads 31, 36
Braces 30-31, 36-39, 44
Briggs Wall & Co. 38
Bruzz 42
Buck & Co. 8
Buck & Hickman 12, 56
Buck ii, 4, 18, 20, 28, 38, 44, 68
Buck, G. 34
Buck, George 28
Buck, J. 38, 84
Buck, Joseph 26, 28
Buck, Mrs G. 18
Bung Borer 41
Bung Hole Borer and Reamer 39, 46
Calipers 56
Catalogues 90
Chesterman 51, 56, 88
Chisels 47-48, 67-68
Cider Sampler 80
Clinometers 62-64
Compasses 3
Cox, E. 20
Cramps 2, 82
Creasers 60
Croze or Cheve 39-40
Davis Level & Tool Co. 62-64
Deck Dowelling Bits 48
Dibb, W. 50
Die Stock 88
Disston, Henry, & Sons 4, 8
Dr Bates 63-64
Drills 31-36
Dummy 82
Elliott Lucas Ltd 71, 73
Fagan, W.H., & Son 8
Fillister ii
Firing Iron 80
Fitkin, Robert 20
Flagging Iron 44
Frenzel, Rudolf 66
Gardner, T.F. 46
Gauges 51-52, 56, 75
Gilpin, W. 50
Gleave, J., & Sons 24
Glue Pots 43, 81
Greaves, William 44
Hammers 82, 85-86
Hammond & Hussey Ltd 22
Haring, W.H. 63-64
Heyes, J. 12
Hildick, G.T. 22
Hinge or Butt Seating Cutting Machine 67, 70
Hollows & Rounds 18
Hoop Driver 44
Humphris & Son 1, 12
Ibbotson, Thos. 36
Ibbott, A.R. 71-72
Jigger 44
Jigger/Router 14
Jointers 26, 46
Jointing Tool 9
Kaye, T.S., & Son 28
Kelly & Sons 54
Knives 44, 54
Langley, Wm., & Co. 44
Lasting Pincers 60
Lathe 88-89
Levels 29, 63-66
Lilleyman 82
Maddin J.G. 40
Madox, William 20
Mallets 47, 50, 57, 82
Marples, Robert 38
Marples, William 9, 18, 36, 38
Marples, William, & Sons 1, 4, 22
Marshall, Alex 64
Masette 85, 87
Mathieson, A., & Son 50
McCormick 75, 78
McKeand 82
Miller Falls 33-34
Mortice Machine 70
Moseley & Son 20, 22
Moss, William 20
Moulding Tools 76
Mower Blade Grinder 75, 78
Norris ii, 22, 28
Nurse, C. 3
Oak Witchett 78
Patent Office Papers 71, 89
Peugeot Frères 16
Planes ii, 11, 15-28, 33, 40, 47-50, 53, 57-60, 74, 79, 87
Pliers 71, 73, 88
Plumb Bob and Reel 64
Preston, E., & Sons 10, 16
Preston, W. 66
Prickers 59-60
Pugh, E., & Co. 81
Punches 59-60
Rabone, J., & Sons 3, 56, 58, 65-66
Rabone, John, & Son 52, 54
Rawlplug 32
Read 44
Reamley & Wood 78
Redlich, J. 24
Riveting Bits 46
Rounders 26
Rounds 18
Routers 14, 20
Rules 3, 23, 27, 29, 51-52, 54-58
Saw Sets 10-12
Saws 1-12, 89
Scissors 82
Scorpes 42
Scraper 80
Scratch Stock 82
Screw Boxes 84
Scribing Gouge 68
Scythe 76
Sharpening Stone ii
Shaves ii, 3, 15-16, 82
Shaw & Co. 22
Sheep Shears 13
Shepley, William 20
Shiv 40
Socket Brushing Hook ii
Sorby, I. & H. 18, 22, 46
Sorby, I. 35, 50
Sorby, Isaac 28
Spanners 71-72, 89
Spear & Jackson 1, 4, 12, 86
Spiers, Stewart 24
Squares 43, 45, 52
Stanley 24, 26, 74
Stanley Rule & Level Co. 18, 20, 26
Street, H.J. 76
Super Cutawl Minor Jigsaw 78
Supertools Ltd 78
Swift 42
Swift, William ii
Sym, I. 20
Trouser Sticks 52
Tape Measures 51, 54-56, 66, 88
Terry, Albert V. 71-72
Timber Scribes 54
Timmins & Sons 86
Tool Chest 76
Trammels 58
Traveller 39-40
Turner, T. 78
Turnscrews 85-86
Twybill or Besaigue 67-68
Vices 14, 80
Waller Tool Co. 70
Ward 18, 24, 28, 47, 68
Washer Cutter 81
Watch Mainspring Winder 75, 80
Wire Strippers 73
Wood Smoother ii
Wrenches 71-72, 88
Wynn & Timmins 60, 81, 88